Encyclopedia of the Animal World

7 *Dog—Environment*

Bay Books Sydney

OG, a general term referring to several species in the family Canidae, including the olf *Canis lupus,* coyote *Canis latrans,* mestic dog *Canis familiaris* and four ecies of *jackal. Other members of this mily, which arose about ten million years ;o, are referred to as foxes although some, pecially those from South America, cannot sily be ascribed to dogs or foxes. All canids ve an acute sense of smell and hearing, but e dogs more than the foxes are specialized r a surface-dwelling life and reliance on eed and endurance for hunting prey. The riability in size, shape and colouring both ithin and between species in the Canidae is lique among the mammals. For example, olves from the same litter may differ dically in temperament and external opearance. This diversity is based on a vast ne pool. The success of this family with a orld-wide distribution covering many types habitats, is due to this polymorphism. Man mself has used this diversity in selective eeding and today there are more than 100 fferent breeds of domestic dogs.

Two wild dogs which in certain respects emplify the variation within the Canidae e the Cape hunting dog *Lycaon pictus* and e Raccoon dog *Nyctereutes procyonoides* ee also wolf, coyote, jackals, dhole, and ushdog). The Cape hunting dog, a predator aming the savannahs of central and south-n Africa, is a large canid, weighing 60–100 (27–45 kg), with a short sleek coat marked ith large blotches of brown, yellow and hite. The pattern of the coat differs from dividual to individual, the only constant arkings being the white-tipped tail and dark out. The ears are outstandingly big and ounded and the muzzle, short and powerful-oking. Because of peculiarities in the shape f its teeth, the Cape hunting dog has been garded as related to the small bushdog *peothos venaticus,* from Central and South merica, and the dhole *Cuon alpinus,* of sia, but recent studies suggest that these ree species may have developed similarities rough having parallel habits and diet. The unting dogs have also retained five digits on eir forefeet, a primitive trait not found in ther canids.

Cape hunting dogs typically breed once a ear but there is no fixed season. Cubs may be orn between April and June and August and Iovember. The gestation period is 70–71 ays, about one week longer than most wild r domestic dogs.

The Cape hunting dog is a pack hunter, pecialized for preying on the large hoofed ammals of the African plains. Pack size anges from 3–50 animals, but more often is etween 12 and 20. Hunts usually take place t dawn and dusk, when the pack will travel ogether towards a herd of wildebeest, zebra, uffalo or gazelles. When the herd is at hand, ne or two dogs will select a single animal and

begin chasing it. The remainder of the pack do not follow closely, but station themselves at various distances to ensure that any quarry circling back will be cut off. The leaders of the hunt can outrun most prey and begin to nip and bite the hindquarters of the victim when they have caught up with it. The prey weakened, the other pack members close in for the kill. The dogs then tear the prey apart, sometimes without killing it before-hand. Most of the carcass is eaten immediately, and soon after, the pack returns to the den or settles in a favourite rest site.

Cape hunting dogs have a highly developed social life where the needs of the individual are subordinate to the needs of the group. When a female is rearing cubs, the pack members all bring food back to the den. Moreover, Cape hunting dogs have developed an unusual feeding ritual derived from the infantile pattern of begging for food. Each individual begs another to regurgitate meat by pushing at its snout and licking its lips. In this way, partly digested food passes from one dog to another until all are fed. There is no rigid hierarchy or rank order although one male usually shows more leadership qualities than the others. Nursing females are dominant over other animals.

Among themselves, hunting dogs are extremely friendly, especially before the hunt when pack members chase each other play-fully until everyone joins together in a greeting ceremony uttering a peculiar twitter-ing sound. Despite the complexity of their social life, Cape hunting dogs do not use specialized facial expressions to communi-cate with their fellows.

The Raccoon dog is strikingly different from the Cape hunting dog, both in appear-ance and behaviour. A relatively small animal weighing 10–20 lb (4·5–9·5 kg), the Rac-coon dog often increases in weight to 35 lb (16 kg) since it becomes lethargic during the winter months in its northern range (this is not true hibernation). Although called the Raccoon dog because of the black or brown facial mask reminiscent of the North American raccoon *Procyon lotor,* this species is readily distinguished from the latter be-cause its tail has a lengthwise black stripe instead of the raccoon's black tail bands.

Found mainly in the temperate Asian forests, the Raccoon dog has been introduced into Eastern Europe and recently has ex-tended its range westward to Germany. Being of small size, it preys largely on rodents and other small mammals, and is even said to be fond of fish. When little meat is available, it will resort to eating fruits and vegetables, a habit it shares with most foxes and some dogs. Raccoon dogs hunt at night and rest during the day in burrows or naturally-formed shelters. They rarely excavate their own dens, more often taking over vacated fox or badger dens. The tendency to defend a territory is strong, and both males and females urinate and deposit faeces through-out their home range, especially around the den area. Raccoon dogs live in pairs and although not as gregarious as wolves or Cape hunting dogs, mated pairs tend to exhibit much attachment to each other. They often 'hibernate' together and will nearly always sleep curled up against one another. Mates will groom each other by nibbling and licking

Dingo, the wild dog of Australia, believed to be a feral domestic dog.

the face, particularly in the area surrounding the facial mask while other social canids like wolves rarely indulge in mutual grooming.

The breeding season of the Raccoon dog falls in early spring. Shortly before, as they emerge from the winter lethargy, there is an increase in social activity between a pair. One of the Raccoon dog's most interesting displays is seen at this time; the tail is raised to an inverted-U while the black hairs of the tail stripe are erected to form a comb-like effect. Among the canids, only the Bat-eared fox has a similar tail posture.

After the birth of 3–7 cubs, both parents guard and rear the young until they become self-supporting when 4–5 months old. The family may remain together during the winter, but the cubs often leave before the cold sets in.

Neither the Cape hunting dog nor the Raccoon dog are closely related to domestic dogs, but they do demonstrate the degree of diversity within the Canidae. Indeed, it is just this variability which makes the identification of the domestic dog's true ancestor so difficult. Because certain subspecies of Golden jackal Canis aureus, wolf, and coyote show overlap in the size and shape of the skull and skeleton, it is not possible accurately to pinpoint the wild dog which modern breeds most closely resemble.

The three possible ancestors of the domestic dog are the wolf, a wolf and Golden jackal cross, and a now extinct wild canid resembling the Pariah dogs and dingos. Most zoologists believe that the numerous breeds were developed from different subspecies of Asian and European wolf, but jackal and coyote blood could have been added by crossing already domesticated animals with wild ones. With no fossil evidence to support the third theory, it must be discounted for the moment although differences in social behaviour between dingos and wolves support this last hypothesis. Foxes could not have played a role in the development of modern dog breeds since attempts to cross them with dogs and wolves have proved unsuccessful.

A second unanswered question is whether domestication occurred only once or independently in several regions. Fossil evidence suggests that the process began 10,000 to 15,000 years ago. Several dog skeletons dated about 8,000 BC have been found in Central and Northern Europe, Asia, and the Middle East, suggesting that domestication took place towards the end of the Mesolithic in these localities. These dog skeletons differ from those of known wild species through their smaller teeth, shorter (sometimes longer) muzzles and smaller size.

The reasons for the taming and selective breeding of wild dogs are complex and probably depended on the needs of Mesolithic and Neolithic man in different environments. The initial motivating factor might have been

the use of the dog as food. Many primitive peoples today eat dogs, as did some ancient peoples. Once an association developed between man and dog, the value of dogs in other spheres was no doubt soon recognized. Hunters and gatherers learned to exploit the keen senses of their tamed, but still wild-born, captives in the pursuit of game. Wild dogs scavenging around human settlements in search of refuse not only had a sanitary function but also unconsciously acted as guards by howling and barking when unfamiliar animals or men approached. As selection for behavioural and physical characters continued, dogs assumed importance as sled or draught animals, for herding and protecting domestic livestock and for guarding homes. The dog's role as a home companion probably developed late.

By the early Neolithic period, when agriculture was spreading throughout Asia, the Middle East and Europe, several distinct breeds existed. One, found in Northern Europe, resembles the huskies and may be ancestral to them. A second, from the lake settlements of Switzerland, was a small house dog from which Pomeranians may have been derived. A skeleton found near Moscow is similar to modern dingos while one from the Rhine Valley resembles modern sheepdogs.

When written history and the depiction of animals in art commenced, there were already dogs which cannot be distinguished from modern breeds. The animal-loving Egyptians possessed many types, including mastiffs, terriers, pointers and Pariah dogs (imported from the Far East). Greyhounds were particularly popular, as shown on slate tablets 6,000 years old. Some Egyptian Pharaohs are reported to have housed thousands of dogs in their kennels, undoubtedly an expensive undertaking in ancient times. Favoured pets were often mummified and buried with their masters.

In the Far East other breeds developed, but most care and attention was devoted to producing a pug-nosed dog resembling a lion. Tibetan monks first bred these dogs because lions became an important religious symbol after the rise of Buddhism in 700 BC and there were no true lions in this area of Asia. The Chinese emperors further perfected the lion dogs and developed the Pekingese which was used in the great palaces on both religious and official occasions.

The classification of breeds differs from country to country and usually reflects the main dog interests of each nation. Breeds are normally grouped according to their function, but since this often varies with the locality, it is impossible to provide a classification which satisfies everyone. A recent one has attempted to classify dogs according to their probable origin, but this is unsatisfactory because we know the ancestry of only a few. Man has been trading and crossing dogs for

centuries. Thus, most breeds are of untraceable and mixed origins.

The six main groupings of the America Kennel Club are:

1) Sporting breeds: These include the retrievers, spaniels, setters and pointers, all which were developed as bird or gun dog The spaniels are the oldest and most bas group from which the others have be derived. Retrievers are of recent origin an have been bred mainly in England and Nor America.

2) Hounds: The hounds are divided into tw groups, those that hunt by scent and tho that use sight. In the first are the bloo hounds, beagles and foxhounds, used not on for tracking small carnivores like badgers a foxes, but also criminals. The sight hound including the greyhounds, Afghans, saluk and borzois, are an ancient group of differe ancestry from the scent dogs. Indeed, th saluki is said to be the oldest purebred do having been kept in the Middle East f thousands of years. These breeds we developed in the open country and, bein specialized for a cursorial life, they a unsurpassed for their speed and enduranc Also included among the hounds by th American Kennel Club are the dingo-typ dogs, for example, the Rhodesian ridgebac so-called because of its shoulder patch erect hair, and the barkless African basenji.

3) Working dogs: These are usually divide into herding, guard and sled dogs. Like th hounds, this group is of mixed ancestry. distinction is normally made between th exclusively herding breeds like the colli breeds like the Alsatian and Old Englis sheepdog which both herd and guard an finally those that guard livestock like the S Bernard and the Pyrenean mountain dog. Th latter group also watch over property as d the Alsatians and Doberman pinschers use widely in police work. The sled dogs of arcti regions include the Alaskan huskies, th malamute and the samoyed. Among th working dogs are found the largest breed the St. Bernard for example, weighs 150–20 lb (68–90 kg).

4) Terrier breeds: Terriers were initially use to flush badgers and foxes from their dens. C recent origin, the majority of breeds hav been developed in the British Isles, and ar often named after the regions and cities wher they were first bred. Terriers are known fo their persistence and aggressiveness.

5) Toy dogs: Most members of this group ar just smaller editions of a normal-sized bree and are valued as home companions or 'la dogs'. Among them are the Pekingese, th Mexican hairless dog, the Maltese, the York shire terrier and the griffon from Belgium The smallest dog is the chihuahua weighin only 3–5 lb (1·5–2·5 kg).

6) Non-sporting breeds: Like the toy dogs this group contains mainly housebound

A pack of Cape hunting dogs at their kill. They work as a team, usually between 12 and 20 but sometimes as many as 50. They run down their prey, large hoofed mammals like wildebeest, zebra, buffalo or gazelle, and terrorize the district when hunting.

breeds and show animals, mostly of different ancestry. Included are the Dalmatian, chow-chow and poodle, originally a sporting dog.

Despite enormous differences between individual breeds in appearance and temperament, dogs readily recognize one another as conspecifics when they meet. The reasons are varied, but two stand out. First, dogs have an excellent sense of smell and no matter what the breed, a dog recognizes the scent of another dog. Second, all dogs have certain motor patterns easily interpreted by others, especially during social interactions. Most of these, like rapid tail-wagging to indicate friendliness and snarling or growling which signify threat, are like the social behaviour patterns of wolves. In fact, dogs and wolves, despite their radically different life styles today, share the same basic behaviour repertoire. Both species are territorial and drive strangers from their homes. On unfamiliar ground, however, they are more tolerant which explains the absence of aggression when two dogs meet in the street or a park. Wolves and dogs regularly deposit urine and faeces on bushes, posts and rocks within their home range. Males always lift a hindleg before urinating, a response which appears at sexual maturity and is dependent on the presence of the male hormone

testosterone. This tendency to distribute scent marks throughout the territory is strong, and careful training is necessary to restrict the activities of housebound dogs. Individuals can almost certainly distinguish the scent marks of neighbours. A bitch in heat has a strongly-scented urine which is readily recognized by males.

If allowed to run wild in groups, a dog litter will develop the same social structure as a wolf pack. Close relationships develop between individuals and all members of the pack will be loyal to and obey the dominant animal. If a litter is split up early enough and the pups exposed to men, this loyalty is transferred to a human master. Dogs not given contact with man before 14 weeks old are almost untameable and very fearful, thus indicating that dogs have no special affinity with man despite thousands of years of close association.

Many wolf-like traits arising from a cooperative pack hunting life have been exploited by man for his own needs. Dogs hunt both individually and in packs and will also retrieve game, a behaviour recalling the wolf's tendency to carry prey back to the den. The tracking abilities of dogs have been employed in finding hidden criminals and discovering buried mines during wartime.

Guiding the blind which relies on the dog's loyalty and specialized senses is a recent and very worthwhile use of the dog.

As a result of domestication, the reproductive cycle of the dog has been altered in ways that increase its reproductive potential. Sexual maturity occurs earlier in domestic dogs than their wild counterparts, at one year instead of two years of age. Moreover, bitches come into heat twice a year at any season (except the basenji), and males are able to mate at any time unlike the annually breeding wild dogs and foxes. The litter size of a domestic bitch is also larger than a wolf. It is probable that these changes have occurred through selective breeding, a constant supply of nutritious food, and reduced exposure to severe fluctuations in weather.

Before coming into heat, a bitch usually has a blood-tinged discharge from the vulva for one to two weeks. During this period, males show increasing interest in her and often invite play by springing up and down on the forelegs in front of her while cocking the head to one side. This form of courtship leads to attempted mounts, but a bitch will not allow mating until she reaches full oestrus. Once receptive, the female stands and twists the tail to one side, thus exposing the vulva to any male. During heat, lasting about a week,

pug

mastif

newfoundland

St. Bernard

alsatian

collie

bouvier

corgi

Fox terrier

Airdale terrier

Cairn terrier

Bedlington terrier

Golden retriever

pointer

Cocker spaniel

dachshound

frequent matings will occur if the bitch is given access to a male. Copulation in dogs is unusual in that the pair becomes locked together or 'tied', usually for 15–20 minutes, although ties as long as an hour have been recorded. During mating, the male dismounts and turns around so that he and the female face away from each other. The gestation of the dog, like the wolf and coyote. is about 63 days. Occasionally, when females have not been fertilized they will show all the characteristics of pregnancy, such as swelling of the abdomen and lactation, without being gravid, a condition known as pseudo-pregnancy or false pregnancy.

The maternal behaviour of the bitch consists of grooming and suckling the young, retrieving them when they wander from the den, and keeping them warm. Puppies are completely helpless at birth, being both blind and deaf, and depend on the mother to fulfil all needs. At 14 days the eyes open, but it is three to four weeks before the pups show much activity other than sleeping and sucking. By six weeks old, they are displaying social responses to each other and to humans. This is a critical period in a dog's develop-

boxer

bulldog

Dobermann pinscher

schnauzer

husky

samoyed

chowchow

keeshond

borzoi

whippet

afghan

Gordon setter

bloodhound

pekinese

maltese

Miniature poodle

nent; should a pup be isolated from contact with dogs or humans at this stage, his social responsiveness may be permanently impaired as an adult. In fact, most training begins during this period since pups are most labile and approachable between 6 and 12 weeks old and do not display fear to unknown situations until 12–14 weeks.

The long and continued association

There is no general agreement, as from country to country, on how breeds of domestic dogs should be classified. Here 32 breeds only are illustrated and roughly classified as follows, reading left to right and top to bottom: 1–6 bulldog-like dogs, 7–8 pinschers and schnauzers, 9–12 sheepdogs, 13–16 spitz hounds, 17–20 terriers, 21–23 longlegged hounds, 24–29 hunting dogs, 30–32 toy dogs.

between man and dog is one of the most extraordinary in the animal world. These two separate species can understand and respond to each other's moods as well as share experiences during work and play. Calling the

dog 'man's best friend' may sound like a cliché, but it expresses the importance of the dog's role in the life of *Homo sapiens*. FAMILY: Canidae, ORDER: Carnivora, CLASS: Mammalia.   D.G.K.

Lesser spotted dogfish swimming in the aquarium at the Plymouth Biological Station.

Egg of the Lesser spotted dogfish fixed to Sea fan *Eunicella verrucosa* by the long tendrils from each corner of the capsule.

DOG'S KEEN NOSE. We often take it for granted that dogs have a very keen sense of smell and can be used for tracking escaped prisoners or lost objects, but several experiments have been made to find out just how sensitive are their noses. One of the first experiments was carried out by G. J. Romanes in 1885. He led a line of 12 men, each putting his feet into the footprints of the preceding man. After a while the party split in two but Romanes' dog was later able to follow her master's trail although 11 other scents were superimposed on his and she followed the right trail without a check where the party split. In other experiments the party contained two identical twins and the dog was able to distinguish between the two if one went each way when the party split up. On the other hand, when given the scent of one twin it would follow a trail made by the other. This suggests that the dog's scent discrimination was about as sensitive as our visual discrimination, as we can often distinguish identical twins provided that we see both at once.

DOGFISHES, small sharks of four quite distinct families. The Smooth dogfishes or hounds (family Triakidae), the Spiny dogfishes (family Squalidae) and the Spineless dogfishes or Sleeper sharks (family Dalatiidae) are dealt with elsewhere. The true dogfishes belong to the family of Cat sharks (Scyliorhinidae) and are characterized by having two dorsal fins, which lack a spine in front, and one anal fin. A spiracle is present but there is no nictitating membrane or 'third eyelid'. The two most common European species are the Greater spotted dogfish *Scyliorhinus stellaris* and the Lesser spotted dogfish *S. caniculus*. The former, which is also known as the nursehound or bullhuss, can be distinguished by the fact that its nostrils are farther apart and the nasal lobes or flaps of skin leading from the nostrils back

towards the mouth are distinctly lobed. In both species the body is generally light brown with a fine speckling of black on the upper surfaces, the spots being larger in the Greater spotted dogfish. The two are very common along all European coasts. They feed on worms, molluscs, crustaceans and echinoderms, and can be fished for by boat over sandy bottoms using lugworms (*Arenicola*) or small pieces of fish. There is an angling record of just over 20 lb (9 kg) for a Larger spotted dogfish caught in British waters. The dogfishes are oviparous and produce rectangular egg cases with a spiralling tendril at each corner. The embryo is well supplied with yolk and does not hatch for seven months after fertilization. FAMILY: Scyliorhinidae, ORDER: Pleurotremata CLASS: Chondrichthyes.

DOGFISHES, are standard animals for dissection in biology classes. The usual dissections are to show the organs of digestion, excretion and reproduction, the gills and their blood supply and the cranial nerves. The advantage for classroom work lies in the dogfishes' simple anatomy and in their abundance. 'The dogfish' which is so familiar as a formalin-reeking carcase to so many students may be one of several species. In British classrooms it is the Lesser spotted dogfish, while on the Pacific coast of the United States students are supplied with Spiny dogfishes. In Britain and the United States dogfish are now marketed for human consumption as 'Rock salmon' and 'grayfish' respectively.

DOG TICK, BROWN *Rhipicephalus sanguineus*, one of 60 species of hard tick. It is one of the most widely distributed of all ticks and its principal host is the dog, although it is known to attack numerous other animals including man. There are four stages in the life-cycle: the egg, larva, nymph and adult. Each of the three active stages feeds on an appropriate host and then drops to the ground, hence the reference to them as three-host ticks. The entire life-cycle can be completed in two months. This species is widely known as a vector of malignant jaundice of dogs and in the Middle East is considered to be the principal vector of boutonneuse fever. See also ticks. FAMILY: Ixodidae, ORDER: Mestigmata, CLASS: Arachnida, PHYLUM: Arthropoda.

DOLIOLUM, a genus of small aquatic animals living in the surface plankton of the oceans and feeding upon plant plankton. They are barrel-shaped and chiefly notable for the extreme complexity of their life-history. The oozooid, the individual which hatches from the egg, lacks sexual organs, but buds off a series of phorozooids, somewhat

Pacific striped dolphin, is found in the northern Pacific as far south as California in large, socially organized schools.

similar in appearance to itself. Both oozooid and phorozooid are less than $\frac{1}{10}$ in (2 mm) long at first, and the former never exceeds this size, but the latter may eventually grow to $\frac{1}{2}$ in (12 mm). It serves chiefly as a means of budding off the next generation of zooids, the blastozooids, which alone possess gonads and are capable of sexual reproduction. The long chain of blastozooids trails behind the muscular phorozooid, now known as an 'old nurse' and connected to its blood system. The old nurse no longer feeds, but is fed by its chain of diminutive blastozooids, while it provides most of the muscle power. See also Sea squirts and Thaliacea. FAMILY: Doliolidae, CLASS: Thaliacea, SUBPHYLUM: Urochordata, PHYLUM: Chordata.

DOLPHINS, marine fishes of tropical and subtropical oceans. The head is large and the body tapers gracefully to the tail, which is strongly forked. The long dorsal fin and the back are a superb green and the flanks and tail have an orange band. Young dolphins are marked with a series of black vertical bars. The Common dolphin *Coryphaena hippurus* grows to 5 ft (1·5 m), the males being larger than the females. It can swim at 37 mph (59 kph) and is well able to catch Flying fishes, on which it feeds voraciously. Other fish are also eaten. The only other member of this family is the Pompano dolphin *C. equiselis,* a smaller fish which only reaches 30 in (75 cm). The Common dolphin has a fast growth rate and a specimen weighing about $1\frac{1}{2}$ lb (0·6 kg) kept at the Florida Marine Studios grew to $37\frac{1}{2}$ lb (16·8 kg) in only $7\frac{1}{2}$ months. FAMILY: Coryphaenidae, ORDER: Perciformes, CLASS: Pisces.

DOLPHINS, a group of small Toothed whales difficult to define accurately. Strictly speaking, the term should be limited to the true dolphins (family Delphinidae), but it would be unreasonable not to include the closely related Long-beaked dolphins (Stenidae). Rather more dissimilar are the River dolphins (Platanistidae). In practice, therefore, the term is used for smaller Toothed whales that are not porpoises. The difficulty surrounding the name dolphin is made greater by the fact that even among the true dolphins there are whales in the generally accepted sense; large animals of over 20 ft (7 m) in length (see whales). A male Killer whale, for instance, may be 30 ft (10 m) long.

Another difficulty, particularly in America, is that the word dolphin tends, in popular language, to be restricted to the game fish dolphins *Coryphaena* and hence cetacean dolphins are popularly called porpoises. But the name porpoise should more properly be restricted to the family Phocaenidae which are all fairly small animals, rarely over 6 ft (2 m) in length, with a rounded head, a mouth with spade-like teeth, a triangular dorsal fin and rather rounded fore-flippers. Dolphins on the other hand usually have conical teeth (when present), commonly a beak-like mouth and a dorsal fin with a curved trailing edge (though some have no dorsal fin).

The best known dolphin is the Bottlenosed dolphin *Tursiops truncatus,* the highly intelligent and friendly creature now so popular in many large aquaria. The Bottlenosed dolphin is moderately large, up to 12 ft (4 m) in length and has a medium-sized beak with 40 teeth in each jaw. It is usually grey on the back but may approach black; the belly, chest and throat are white or pale grey but there is no sharp line between the two shades. It is found on both sides of the North Atlantic and into the Mediterranean. A very similar Bottlenosed dolphin *T. aduncus* is found in the Red

Dolphin in a seaquarium, a familiar sight to visitors over the last 30 years.

Sea, Indian Ocean and around Australia, whilst *T. gilli* is the Pacific form.

The Bottlenosed dolphin is a favourite animal for study in captivity because it is relatively easy to catch, easy to handle in captivity and very tractable, becoming very attached to its human friends if properly treated. It is also easy to train and, therefore, so long as it is not allowed to get bored, it will respond to experimental conditions in much the same way as it does for show purposes. It is highly intelligent and shows remarkable ability at developing ideas, initiating games with attendants. It will even use whatever material is available to serve its purpose. Had it hands it could well be an effective tool-user.

A great deal of our knowledge of dolphins and Cetacea has arisen from the chance to study the Bottle-nosed dolphin under aquarium conditions. Recently the number of species kept under these conditions has increased and a great amount of information has become available. It would be unrealistic to take behavioural studies, in particular, direct from a captive population as a true indication of behaviour in the wild but by comparison with what information can be deduced from the wild an approximation can be made as a basis for further study.

There are said to be 25 species of Long-beaked dolphins in the genus *Stenella* but probably this should be reduced to about ten true species. Even of these some are known only from skulls and within the whole group the skulls tend to show similarities which make formal establishment of species difficult. The Slender dolphin *S. attenuata* is found in warmer parts of the Atlantic, the Spotted dolphin *S. plagiodon* is a deep water species off the North American Atlantic coast, as also is *S. euphrosine*. Other species are found in most of the warmer waters of the world. The Rough-toothed dolphin *Steno bredanensis* is very closely related but it has characteristically rough teeth and is found in the warmer parts of the Atlantic and the Indian Ocean.

Members of the genus *Sotalia* are small dolphins of only about $3\frac{1}{2}$ ft (1 m) long. Four species are found in the Amazon and one in the harbour of Rio de Janeiro. The genus *Sousa,* also long-beaked, is found in tropical waters of the eastern Atlantic, the Indian and Pacific Oceans. It includes *S. teuszii,* found in rivers in Senegal and the Cameroons, which was formerly thought to be the only whale to feed on vegetable material. *S. plumbea* is found off East Africa. The Chinese white dolphin *S. sinensis* is a truly white animal which is found up the Yangtze and other Chinese waters. Very little is known of this genus.

The Common dolphin *Delphinus delphis* is found in large schools in temperate waters throughout the world. It is slender, up to 8 ft (2·4 m) in length and has a pronounced beak. It has a dark grey to black back and a white belly with light grey or brownish stripes on the mouth. The dolphin pictures of classical times usually seem to be of Common dolphins but Bottlenosed dolphins also exist in the Mediterranean. It is a fast swimmer, probably the fastest of all dolphins and is difficult to catch. When caught it has been found to be very nervous and difficult to keep in captivity as it needs to be with its fellows. At sea in freedom and company, however, it is apparently much more confident and will approach boats and even swimmers. The Pacific Common dolphin *D. bairdi* is very similar and is probably a subspecies.

The Irrawaddy dolphin *Orcaella brevirostris* is a beakless dolphin about 7 ft (2·1 m) in length. It has a small dorsal fin, rather long broad flippers and an overall blue-grey colour. It is found in the Irrawaddy over 900 miles (1,400 km) upriver. A rather different dolphin is found in the Bay of Bengal, around Malaya and off Thailand, but it is unlikely to be an entirely different species. The behaviour of both is much the same. They are traditionally adopted by the local fishing communities and, although feeding exclusively on fish themselves, have the reputation for driving fish into nets.

There are two species of Right whale dolphins, so called because they have no dorsal fin like the true Right whales. *Lissodelphis peronii* is found in southern seas around New Zealand and southern Australia. It is a strikingly coloured animal of some 6 ft (1·8 m) length, having the top of the head, back and flukes black and the rest of the body, including the flippers, white. The northern species *L. borealis* is found in the North Pacific. It is rather larger, being over 8 ft (2½ m) and the black extends downwards to include the flippers, leaving white on the chest between the flippers and extending to the tail.

The genus *Cephalorhynchus* consists of about a dozen species none of which is at all well known. Some are known only from skeletons and skulls. They are all found in southern seas and those known in the flesh are all strikingly marked. At first sight they would appear to be porpoises rather than dolphins having little or no beak and porpoise-like flippers and dorsal fins. Only four species are at all well known but even this amounts to carcases or occasional sea sighting.

Heaviside's dolphin *C. heavisidei* was named after Captain Haviside but corrupted by misunderstanding to Heaviside. It is a striking animal of about 4 ft (1·2 m) having a

Similar conditions in a marine environment have led to similar body forms in three totally unrelated animals: a shark, an ichthyosaur and a dolphin. Below: Dolphins emit a wide range of sounds, used for locating prey, navigation, and communicating. The principle is the same as used by submarines: the emitted sound waves (blue closed lines) strike an object and the reflected waves (red dotted lines) are picked up by the dolphin.

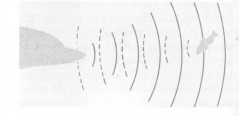

Tursiops catalania, of the Indian Ocean and Australian seas, a near relative of the Bottlenosed dolphin.

black back and a white or yellowish-white undersurface with lobes of white running up onto the side in front of and behind the black flippers and obliquely towards the tail. It is best known around South Africa.

Hector's dolphin *C. hectori* is similarly coloured to Heaviside's but somewhat longer, 6 ft (1·8 m). The black undersides of the flippers extend across the chest and a strip towards the head. It is best known around New Zealand.

Commerson's dolphin *C. commersoni,* of southern South America and the Falkland Islands, is the most striking of all dolphins. It has a black head and flippers, vent, dorsal fin and tail and otherwise is white.

The White-bellied dolphin *C. albiventris* is also found in much the same waters though more rarely seen. It is about $4\frac{1}{2}$ ft ($1\frac{1}{2}$ m) long and black with white on the throat, behind the flippers and belly.

Externally, the genus *Lagenorhynchus* can be compared with the above group, but there are differences in the bones of the skull and particularly the large number of vertebrae, which may be as many as 90. They have fairly large and characteristically dolphin type dorsal fins with a concave posterior border. The genus is represented in the colder seas of both the northern and southern

hemispheres and one species is particularly well known, having been kept in captivity to a considerable extent.

Wilson's hour-glass dolphin *L. wilsoni* is seen only in the Antarctic along the edge of the pack ice. It is remarkable for its clear black and white colouring, which gives an hour-glass effect, of white on the flanks and a white belly and tail to the black flukes.

The Cruciger dolphin *L. cruciger* is also rarely seen. Very striking white bands on its flanks produce a cross-like effect. The first whole animal, from the South Pacific, only recently became available for study. Fitzroy's dolphin *L. fitzroyi* and Peak's dolphin (or porpoise) *L. autralis* are also rarely seen.

The Dusky dolphin *L. obscurus* is the best known southern species. It is the commonest dolphin around New Zealand where it is found in large schools but extends across to the Falkland Islands and to South Africa. It is black and white with black back, mouth, eye, flippers and tail but with white bands coming from the belly giving a marvellous effect. Lillie, in the 'Terra Nova' Report on Cetacea, states 'This dolphin does not seem to occur further south than about Lat. 58° S, but when we were approaching, or leaving, the coast of New Zealand we invariably met large schools of Dusky dolphin which used to follow us and

play around the bows of the ship, as though they were seeing us off or welcoming us back to the temperate lands'. Several other southern species are known only from skeletal material.

The three northern species are somewhat longer being up to 10 ft (3 m) in length, as compared with 7 ft (2·1 m) for the Dusky dolphin and 5–6 ft (1·7 m) for the others. They are all somewhat similar in appearance and behaviour and probably are quite closely allied.

The Bottlenosed dolphin, often called a porpoise.

Spotted dolphin *Stenella plagiodon*, of the Atlantic.

Bottlenosed dolphin performing in a seaquarium. Dolphins seem to show a sense of endeavour.

The White-sided dolphin *L. acutus* is black dorsally and white bellied with a prominent white streak on its flank. It lives in the North Atlantic where its range extends from Greenland in the north across to Norway, where it is the second most common dolphin, north British waters and Cape Cod, off America. It is highly gregarious, being found in schools of up to 1,500 animals.

The White-beaked dolphin *L. albirostris* is similar to the White-sided dolphin but has a characteristic white beak. The margin of the upper lip is grey or black and the lower lip may also show some colour as well. It is also found in vast schools in the North Atlantic extending over much the same areas as the White-sided dolphin. The young of both species are born in the spring and early summer and the mating season probably occurs at the same time of year.

The Pacific striped dolphin *L. obliquidens* is very similar in appearance to the White-sided dolphin and is found in the northern Pacific as far south as California. This animal is also found in large, socially organized schools. It is fairly easily caught and has proved a popular dolphin attraction in captivity. Hose's Sarawak dolphin *Lagenodelphis hosei* is only known from a single specimen sent as a skeleton to England in 1895 and was about 8 ft (2·4 m) long. It appears to be midway between the *Lagenorhynchus* and *Delphinus* dolphins but no others have been seen.

Risso's dolphin *Grampus griseus* is perhaps unfortunately named, because a common name for the Killer whale is 'grampus'. There is, however, no similarity in appearance or behaviour between the two animals. It is said that the word 'grampus' is an abbreviation of *grand poisson*. Risso's dolphin is a longish, beakless dolphin of about 12–13 ft (4 m) in length. It is grey and may be black on the fin, flippers and tail whilst the underside is paler to lighter grey or even white. Often the skin shows white score marks which are said to be healed tooth marks of other Risso's dolphins. It is very widely distributed in the North Atlantic and the Mediterranean and in the south around New Zealand and South Africa. It is fairly solitary, rarely being found in schools of more than a dozen. It feeds mainly on cuttlefish.

The famous Pelorus Jack was a Risso's dolphin which frequented the Pelorus Sound between Nelson and Wellington, New Zealand, where it swam at the bows of ships for 24 years. It became so famous that museums, as well as fishermen, wanted to catch it but it was so popular with sailors and people around the straits that it was protected by Order-in-Council, viz. '—it shall not be lawful for any person to take the fish or mammal of the species commonly known as Risso's dolphin (*Grampus griseus*) in the waters of Cook Strait, or of the bays, sounds and estuaries adjacent thereto.' The order lasted for five years in each case and was repeated four times until Pelorus Jack disappeared. See Killer whales, Pilot whales, River dolphins and Toothed whales. FAMILIES: Delphinidae and Stenidae, ORDER: Cetacea, CLASS: Mammalia.   K.M.B.

DOLPHINS IN DISTRESS. There have been many stories of dolphins helping their wounded companions, holding them up to the surface so that they can breathe, and there are even reports of drowning men being rescued by dolphins. At first these stories tended to be treated with scepticism by zoologists but since dolphins have been kept in oceanaria they have been found to be remarkably intelligent. Helping an injured companion, known as epimeletic behaviour, was recorded in an oceanarium when a Bottle-nosed dolphin was accidentally knocked unconscious. Its two companions lifted it to the surface so that it could breathe, but every once in a while they released it so that they could breathe themselves.

In 1969 there was a report of such behaviour in the wild. A Common dolphin was harpooned from a research ship and six dolphins came to its rescue. They lifted it to the surface twice, but after that it was lost to sight. Such altruistic behaviour is not always shown for sometimes the distress calls of a wounded dolphin cause the rest of the school to flee from it.

Rescue behaviour has been seen in the Bottlenosed dolphin *Tursiops truncatus,* the Common dolphin *Delphinus delphis* and in the Pacific whitesided dolphin *Lagenorhynchus obliquidens.*

DOMESTICATION. Domestic animals are those kept by man to perform some service

for him. He assumes responsibility for their feeding and protection and also determines the lines along which they will breed. In many places these animals have become an indispensible part of the human economy, and in their turn have come to rely on man so completely that they often cannot survive if released into the wild. Both man and animal thus benefit from the association, and we could well define domestication as a symbiosis directed by man.

Man alone does not conform to the principle of 'adaptation to environment'. Instead, he seeks to adapt his environment to suit himself. Domestication, particularly of cattle, represents the most important step taken in this exploitation of the animal world, but the nature and times of its origins are obscure. The archaeological evidence of early domestication is confusing and subject to different interpretations. Indeed, from fragmentary bone remains it is difficult to determine whether an animal was domesticated or not, and much reliance has to be placed on the evidence of carvings and decorated pottery.

The earliest men were nomadic and probably had only sheep, goats and dogs as

company. Later, with the development, in the Mesolithic, of agricultural practices, man became sedentary, with fixed settlements and cultivated crops. These brought about the contact between man and animals. Pigs scavenging the village refuse heaps, wild cattle raiding crops, provided the opportunities for their capture and subsequent domestication. Furthermore, only after the development of agricultural practices could man produce sufficient spare food to feed domestic beasts. The domestication of some species was well advanced over 3,000 years ago and recent excavations in southern Turkey suggest that some animals may have been domesticated twice as long ago. Certainly, Neolithic Man in Europe had domestic cattle, goats, sheep, pigs and dogs.

Although agricultural people tamed many species, certain important domestications originated in other ways, notably in the case of the horse and reindeer. Careless cultivation and overgrazing meant that the early agriculturalists who lived in areas of poor soil, ruined their territory and had to move on to new lands periodically, a process still regrettably evident even today. The horse was probably first domesticated as a beast of

Domesticated asses or donkeys are much maligned but highly valuable beasts of burden.

burden to help in the job of moving camp regularly. In the case of the reindeer, man has become virtually a social parasite on the herds, following them about the whole time, as they live their natural unrestricted lives, simply taking from the herds what he wants when it is needed.

Most of the important domestic animals lived in herds when wild and are used to following a leader and keeping together. It was inevitable that man should usurp the position of herd leader, the animals becoming accustomed to being in company with humans as well as their own species.

Today almost all domestic animals are bred in captivity. New generations are not derived afresh from wild progenitors except in the case of the elephant. When domestication was first being developed, however, the process had to start at the beginning, with the capture of suitable wild animals, which were gradually tamed. This was best done with young animals. The next stage had to be a change in temperament allowing a captive animal to accept its new surroundings so completely that it would actually breed. The third stage was to choose from among the stock those individuals with the most desirable characteristics and breed only from these. Selective breeding represents the total control by man of a species' destiny, the very essence of domestication, allowing animals to be 'tailor made' for specific purposes as in cattle which are used essentially to turn fodder into money via meat or dairy produce.

Domestication has physical effects on animals. The skull shows signs of arrested development and becomes wide with a short snout and jaws, as in the domestic pig. There is a general decrease in size, making the animals easier to handle. Modern cattle, for example are only 4 ft (1·3 m) high, whereas the ancestral aurochs were over 6 ft (2 m) tall. Later selective breeding can encourage the development of larger varieties if these are needed, for example, for extra pulling power in draft horses or extra meat in sheep and pigs. The size of the ears and eyes tends to decrease under domestication, presumably because they are no longer vital for warning of the approach of predators. Temperamental changes centre around the endocrine system, in particular a low activity in the adrenal glands making the animals tame and inexcitable, best shown by comparing laboratory rats with the ancestral Brown rat.

In short, domestication encourages the maintenance of an overall infantilism or juvenile state in animals.

Other changes, such as the development of curly instead of straight hair and the appearance of piebald varieties, as in horses and pigs, can be attributed to the partial absence of natural selection in captivity. In the wild, such varieties would be at a disadvantage and would be weeded out by predators. In

captivity they can live and breed, producing great diversity in the stock and thus providing the extreme varieties needed as the basis for selective breeding. Excessive specialization can lead to the formation of almost grotesque animal machines; a cow that is little more than a huge, walking milk producing udder; a sheep with fleece hanging down to the ground; a race horse that is all legs and so highly strung as to be useless for anything except racing; a chicken that does nothing except take in food at one end and push out eggs from the other.

The horse, camel and elephant have been domesticated as sources of power and used for transporting loads too heavy for man to bear. Even today, these animals are vital in many areas unsuitable for the use of lorries and tractors. Dogs render valuable assistance to the hunter or help the shepherd. The pest destroying talents of cats and mongooses are much appreciated and birds have been used in fishing, like the cormorants of Japan, and for falconry.

Certain species have been regarded with great reverence since time immemorial and religious motives may have prompted their domestication. It has been suggested that chickens were originally kept to ward off ghosts. Many animals may first of all have been kept as pets, either in response to human mothering instincts or as playthings for children. This is seen in many primitive societies today where monkeys, parrots and almost any reasonably attractive animal, especially young ones, are found living with the humans as family pets. Even in the more advanced countries, pet keeping is a major industry with many domestic strains of cats, dogs, budgerigars, parrots, goldfish and others being produced especially to provide comfort or amusement to people.

Various domestic animals are kept because they have some particular biological features that make them useful in medicine or in biological research. The tame and prolifically breeding Guinea pigs, White rats and mice are used in immense numbers for testing new drugs. Monkeys and horses are important in the production of vaccines. The Fruit fly *Drosophila* has many features which make it an ideal tool for the study of genetics. Even the pig is becoming important in medical spheres, having convenient size and immunological properties for use in organ transplant surgery; and a variety of species have been used to investigate the biological hazards of space travel.

Various mammals have been suggested as likely candidates for developing new domestic species. Among these may be mentioned the eland, a large African antelope, ideally adapted to living in the semi-desert bush and grassland, where domestic cattle have a struggle to survive. The eland breeds well in such places and grows into a large animal

whose meat is excellent. Experiments in Poland have aimed at domesticating the elk to pull sledges, carry a rider and produce milk Manatees of South America could well be used to browse and clear the aquatic vegetation that clogs so many canals and waterways, thus turning the waterweed into usable meat. Another suggestion is to train porpoises to locate shoals of fish and herd them as a dog does sheep. To combat the war-time U-boat menace, it was even suggested that seagulls be domesticated and trained to perch on periscopes out at sea, thus revealing the whereabouts of submarines!

There are only two important domesticated invertebrates, the honeybee and the silkworm. Bee keeping was practised by the ancient Egyptians and the keeping of silk worms (sericulture) originated in China over 3,000 years ago. Before the development of the sugar cane and beet industries, honey was the only source of sweetening for human food. Silkworms are truly domesticated in the sense that they cannot live without man's aid Each spins a cocoon, made of several miles of the fine silk thread, in which the larva pupates. Introduced to other places as part of a rich and exclusive industry, silkmoth larvae are reared in large open trays of mulberry leaves until they pupate. The cocoons are then soaked in hot water, unravelled, and the silk thread is collected, spun and woven into cloth.

P.A.M.

DOMINANCE HIERARCHY, can be said to be present in a group of animals when some individuals are able to attack or threaten others without fear of retaliation. In this situation the attacker (or dominant) is said to be of higher rank than the individual which fails to challenge it and which is known as the subordinate. Low ranking animals either avoid high ranking individuals or make some form of appeasement gesture towards them if they come into their proximity.

An example of a dominance hierarchy is that of the Domesticated fowl *Gallus domesticus*. Amongst hens the dominance hierarchy takes the form of a 'peck order'. Hen A pecks B while hen B does not peck A; hen B, however, pecks C which does not peck either A or B. Hen C pecks D, but not A, B and C. This is called a linear hierarchy and its existence is well shown in competitive situations. If the hens are given food scattered on the ground, hen A is always in the best position for feeding and if A is removed, hen B takes on this role.

Religious motives may have prompted the domestication of chickens originally kept to ward off ghosts. The domestic chicken derives probably from only one wild form, the bankiva, but there are now a great number of breeds, a few of which are shown here with dates of origin. The bankiva is bottom.

1. White leghorn, Italy, several centuries old; 2. ancona, Italy, 19th century; 3. Barnyard fowl, the Netherlands, about 1850; 4. Rhode Island red, United States, 1879–1880; 5. wyandotte, United States, 1883; 6. australorp, Australia, 1949; 7. Plymouth rock, United States, 1878; 8. New hampshire, United States, 1915; 9. sussex, England, c. 1903; 10. cochin, China, 19th century.

Konrad Lorenz has described a peck order amongst jackdaws *Corvus monedula* and in this case, the birds pair for life and the female partner takes on the rank of her mate. According to Lorenz, a high-ranking female will not pair with a low-ranking male whereas the reverse is often the case. Furthermore, a formerly low-ranking female takes immediate advantage of her enhanced status and attacks her erstwhile superiors, taking precedence over them in competition for food.

Hierarchies are not always linear as Hall and DeVore discovered in their study of free-living baboons *Papio ursinus*. In this case an alliance between three males enabled them collectively to be dominant over the other adult males because they supported one another in fights. A male stronger than any one of these three existed in the colony but he was unable to become overall dominant as long as his three rivals supported one another if he attacked one of them.

The social groups within the societies of baboons may have different positions in the hierarchy. Adult males are dominant over all other groups, sub-adult males are dominant to females, whilst juveniles are subordinate to all other males and females. Members of these social groups recognize the status of members of other groups, often aided by visual cues. Adult male baboons, for example, are distinguished by their manes and enlarged canine teeth. The older males in a group of gorillas *Gorilla gorilla* have silver-grey hairs on their backs and younger males recognize these individuals as having a high status and do not challenge them.

Changes in the dominance hierarchy normally result from fights between individuals of near-equal status but may also be caused by the entry of a stranger into the group who may successfully challenge the dominant. Changes are also brought about by old age or illness which result in an individual falling to a lower position in the rank order.

The physiological condition of an animal may also alter its status; a female baboon which is in oestrus rises in rank and consorts with high-ranking males. Female baboons with infants also have a higher status than those without. T.B.P.

DONKEY, one of several vernacular names in the English language for the domesticated ass. It seems not to have been in general use until the 18th century and it may be derived from *dun,* the colour of the animal's coat, with *kin* meaning small, and corrupted from this to donkey. See ass.

DORMANCY, a resting condition adopted by many animals at certain times in their lives, usually correlated with the seasons, when growth stops and the internal pro-

cesses of the body are slowed down. This resting state, although always being concerned with survival in adverse conditions, is not always brought about in the same way.

Sometimes the adverse conditions themselves are directly responsible for the reduction in activity. All cold-blooded animals, vertebrate and invertebrate, are dependent on suitable temperatures in their habitats for their normal body processes to continue. When it gets too cold their bodies simply will not work any more and they become dormant. When it gets warm again the animals resume normal activity. In insects this type of dormancy is called 'quiescence'.

Quiescence, or its equivalent, is adequate for survival for relatively short periods of unsuitable conditions, but not for longer ones since the living processes continue during the quiescence and require fuel from food, although much less is needed than in the active animal. Quiescent animals do not build up reserves of food before quiescence begins so that their reserves are inadequate for long survival. Other animals have a dormant period as a normal part of the life-cycle and in this case some preparation is usually made for the adverse conditions before dormancy begins. Very often these preparations involve the laying down of food reserves and seeking out a suitable place in which to rest. In insects this type of dormancy is called 'diapause' while in other animals it may take the form of hibernation or aestivation. It has been suggested that the winter sleep of bears, which is not a true hibernation, should be called winter dormancy.

Dormancy is also, and perhaps more usually, used to refer to the resting stages of plants. See also diapause, hibernation and aestivation. R.F.C.

The Edible dormouse, of Europe.

DORMICE, in general appearance as well a in their way of life, tend to bridge the ga between squirrels and mice. They constitute very distinctive family of rodents, th Gliridae (formerly Muscardinidae), represented by a variety of species throughou Africa and temperate Eurasia. Like squirrel dormice with one exception have bushy tail but they are mostly mouse- rather tha squirrel-sized and, like most mice, they a nocturnal. Dormice are mostly agile climber living in trees or in the shrub layer o woodland. The fur is soft and dense. It varie in colour from orange-brown to grey, an many species have dark marks around th eyes, accentuating the already large eyes. Th feet are well adapted for climbing, with lon flexible toes, and, especially in *Muscardinu* the hindfeet can be turned outwards at righ angles to the body enabling the animal t move confidently on slender twigs.

Dormice resemble squirrels rather tha mice in their teeth, having four cheekteeth i each row, the first being a premolar which ha a milk predecessor. The teeth have transvers ridges but they are rooted and therefore hav a limited life. The food is very varie including both animal and vegetable materia although it is likely that seeds and berrie predominate in the diet of most species.

The dormice of the temperate region ar noted for their hibernation, which begins i October. Like other hibernating animals the become very fat in early autumn and durin hibernation become quite torpid and cold, bu may awaken occasionally. The reputation fo deep sleep is well founded, since even th daily sleep is unusually profound and i accompanied by a distinct fall in bod temperature.

By comparison with the much mor abundant and versatile mice of the familie Muridae and Cricetidae, dormice tend to b more specialized in their habitats and be haviour, and they are generally less abundan Their reproductive rate is lower, usually wit only one or two litters per year, but th scarcity of their remains in the pellets of owl shows that their specialized habits allow the to escape the heavy predation suffered b most other kinds of mice. During hibernatio however, they are vulnerable to mammalia predators like weasels and martens, and it i probably at this time that they suffer th highest mortality.

Unlike other mice, the species of dormic are usually very distinctive and many ar placed in distinct genera. The Hazel dor mouse of Europe (the Common dormouse o Britain) *Muscardinus avellanarius* is one o the smallest and has a distinctive orange brown coat. It lives in dense shrubby under growth where it constructs neat nests, ofte using the shredded bark of honeysuckle. Th

Common dormouse, or Hazel dormouse, seems most of its time to be asleep or about to fall asleep.

argest European species, the Fat dormouse *Glis glis*, is more arboreal, nesting in holes or n exposed positions quite high in the woodland canopy. It is also known as the Edible dormouse, since the Ancient Romans fattened it for the table in special jars.

One of the most attractive of all dormice is the Garden dormouse *Eliomys quercinus*, a European species with a conspicuous black mask and a long tail, bushy only towards the tip. It frequents rocky hillsides as well as woodland and is especially common in the Mediterranean region. By far the most isolated species of this family, geographically speaking, is the Japanese dormouse *Glirulus japonicus*, since dormice are quite absent from the mainland of temperate eastern Asia. The Japanese dormouse is small, lives in montane forests and is one of the very few genera of mammals endemic to Japan. A decidedly aberrant member of the family, and one of the least known, is the Mouse-tailed dormouse *Myomimus personatus* found in Turkmenistan, Iran and Bulgaria. It has a long, almost naked tail and appears to be terrestrial rather than arboreal.

African dormice belong to the genus *Graphiurus* and are found throughout the forest and savannah zones of Africa. Although primarily arboreal, they are frequently found living in the thatch of houses.

Related to the true dormice, but constituting a distinct family, the Platacanthomyidae, are two rather dissimilar species, the Spiny dormouse *Platacanthomys lasiurus*, of southern India, and the Chinese dormouse *Typhlomys cinereus*, of southeastern China. They differ from the other dormice in the absence of premolar teeth, having only three molars in each row as in most other mice. A further aberrant and isolated species is the

Desert dormouse *Selevinia betpakdalaensis*, found in the deserts of Kazakhstan in central Asia and placed in a family of its own, Seleviniidae. Although showing some relationship with other dormice, this species has many characteristics that are convergent with other desert rodents, for example, the exceptionally dense, soft fur, the naked tail and the enormously enlarged auditory bullae of the middle ear. The external pinnae of the ears, on the other hand, are extremely small and scarcely project above the fur. FAMILY: Gliridae, ORDER: Rodentia, CLASS: Mammalia.   G.B.C.

DORSAL LIGHT REACTION, method of ensuring the upright position in an animal. Since, under natural conditions, light falls upon an animal from above it will, if it always turns its back towards the incident light, remain upright, i.e. dorsal side up. There are, of course, other ways in which an animal can sense its orientation; the statocysts of Crustacea have this function among others and the maculae in the sacculus of the inner ear of vertebrates also sense the direction of gravity. But a dorsal light reaction is found in both vertebrates and invertebrates even though they may possess gravity sense organs as well. The light response is mediated through the eyes.

When turned on its side a prawn *Leander xiphias* makes rowing movements with its legs which have the effect of righting it. It behaves in this way even if the light is coming from one side. However, if its statocysts are removed and the animal is turned on its side so that the dorsal side is illuminated, it rests quietly making no attempt to right itself. Normally the gravity sense and the dorsal light reaction act together with equal force on

all the legs to produce an upright posture. If a prawn without statocysts is standing upright on a board and is lit from one side, it tips its body sideways through 45° indicating that the sense of contact and the dorsal light reaction acting in partial opposition produce a compromise posture.

The fish *Crenilabrus* will react rather similarly. If it is illuminated from behind in a dark room it takes a head-up posture aligning its body at 45°, but if the light comes from the side it tips over to the same angle. This is the result of the interaction of the activity of the maculae in its inner ear and the dorsal light reaction. If its inner ear is destroyed the fish lies on its side when illuminated from the side and swims on its back when lit from below.

Other aquatic animals have no gravity sense organs to give a frame of reference, for statocysts occur only in the higher Crustacea and are absent from insects. Thus the Fish louse *Argulus*, when illuminated from below instead of above, turns a somersault and swims upside down.

Flying insects are similar to aquatic ones in that they do not have any way of recognizing whether they are the right way up or not. Dragonflies have a well-developed dorsal light reaction which enables them to fly on an even keel; when they settle they turn their backs to the light wherever it is coming from.

For some animals the dorsal light reaction has become a ventral one. The Nile catfish, for example, habitually swims in a manner which is morphologically the wrong way up. The fish has counter-shading which is reversed (back light and underside dark) thus fitting its upside down position. Behavioural responses of this kind ensure that the caterpillars of *Colias edusa* stand with their dark coloured backs to the light while those of *Smerinthus ocellatus*, with reversed colouration, hang upside down below a leaf stalk influenced by a ventral light reaction.   J.D.C.

DOUC *Pygathrix nemaea*, or Douc langur, one of the leaf-eating monkeys of Southeast Asia. It is a grizzled silver grey with pure white arms, rump and tail, black thighs and hands, and chestnut-red lower hindlegs. See langur.

DOUROUCOULI, or Night monkey, several species of monkeys living in the forests from the Amazon to Central America, with large yellow staring eyes. See New World monkeys.

DOVE, term given to certain species of birds of the family Columbidae, which also includes the pigeons, which the doves closely resemble. There is considerable confusion as to the distinction between pigeons and doves. In everyday parlance the term 'dove' is used for the smaller species of the family such as

Mourning dove *Zenaidura macroura*, of America, at its nest in a cactus.

the Turtle dove *Streptopelia turtur* and the term 'pigeon' is more often applied to larger species such as the Wood pigeon *Columba palumbus*. However, the ancestor of the feral pigeons of towns and cities *Columba livia* is called by ornithologists the 'Rock dove', although it is much more similar in size and appearance to the species called 'pigeons'. Ornithologically there is no difference between pigeons and doves and it would seem reasonable to make size the basis of the term's usage. FAMILY: Columbidae, ORDER: Columbiformes, CLASS: Aves.

DRAGONS, mythical monsters appearing in the legends of many cultures. They appear on Babylonian seals, in the Book of Revelation, in the Anglo-Saxon epic *Beowulf,* in stories from China and Japan and on many standards and badges. In many instances the dragon is a participant in the struggle of good against evil and it is then usually depicted as an evil monster. In China, however, the dragon was the 'bringer of fertilizing rain' and a dragon dance was performed to bring rain. Some dragons were winged and some breathed fire but most had snake-like bodies. The European dragon is based on the python, *draco* being Latin for snake, and was elaborated by mediaeval naturalists who described dragons lying in wait for elephants

and strangling them. The 16th century monument of a giant slaying a dragon in Klagenfurt, Austria, shows a typically reptilian dragon with bats' wings. Its head is, however, modelled on a skull found nearby and preserved in the Town Hall. This is, without doubt, that of a Woolly rhinoceros *Rhinoceros antiquitatis*.

DRAGONETS, flattened, bottom-living fishes, members of *Callionymus* and related genera found along coasts in temperate regions. The name *dracunculus* or 'little dragon' was used by Pliny nearly 2,000 years ago and is an appropriate description of these curious little fishes. The dragonets rarely grow to more than 12 in (30 cm) in length. They have flat, depressed heads and slender bodies, but many are so beautifully coloured that they resemble some of the tropical reef fishes. There are no scales on the body. There is a sharp spine on the preopercular bone of the gill cover and there are two dorsal fins of which the anterior is greatly elongated in the male.

Two species of dragonet are found along European shores, the Common dragonet *Callionymus lyra* and the Spotted dragonet *C. maculatus*. The former is common in the Mediterranean and reaches northwards to Norway, often being found along British

shores. The female is rather dull coloured, but the male is a splendid fish, especially in the breeding season. His back is red-yellow with blue markings and the flanks and lower part of the head are orange, again with blue spots and marks. There are two blue bands along the body and the fins are marked with blue, yellow and green. The differences between the sexes are so striking that they were once thought to be quite different species, the 'sordid' and the 'gemmeous' dragonets. Spawning takes place in spring and summer, the male swimming around the female and displaying with gill covers and fins until the female is sufficiently stimulated. The two then swim together to the surface, close together and with the anal fins forming a gutter into which eggs and sperm are shed. The eggs have honeycomb markings on their surfaces.

The Spotted dragonet is a smaller fish and can be distinguished by the three or four rows of ocellated spots instead of bands along the dorsal fin. The sexes also differ, the male being much more gaudy than the female. Once thought to be quite rare, recent work now suggests that this species has merely been overlooked.

There is a deep water genus *Draconetta* found in the North Atlantic. FAMILY: Callionymidae, ORDER: Perciformes, CLASS: Pisces.

DRAGONFLIES, the robust, winged carnivorous insects that comprise the order Odonata. Adult dragonflies are most often seen flying along the edges of ponds and rivers during sunny weather. They have two pairs of narrow, richly-veined wings, a long slender abdomen and prominent eyes. Features that distinguish dragonflies from

Common dragonets. The male is considerably larger than the female.

our-spotted libellula *Libellula quadrimaculata* lives north of the Arctic Circle.

ther insects are the skewed thorax and orwardly directed legs, the inconspicuous ntennae and the existence of accessory enitalia on the second and third abdominal egments of the male. The larvae (sometimes eferred to as nymphs) are fully aquatic, and ave the labium (second maxillae) highly nodified for seizing prey.

Because they are large, active by day and ften strikingly coloured, dragonflies have aptured man's interest and imagination. In Britain adult dragonflies have long been nown by vernacular names such as horse-tinger, adder-bolt and Devil's darning-eedle, names which reflect their formidable ppearance though not their habits. On the ther hand in North America some larger pecies are appropriately known as Mosquito hawks, and in Holland a migratory species as reklibel.

Distribution. Dragonflies are primarily tropi-al insects but occur in temperate latitudes to he limit of trees. In the northern hemisphere his means that in parts of Canada, Alaska nd Sweden they reach the Arctic Circle. These hardy, northern forms are species of Aeshna, Somatochlora and Leucorrhinia, all enera that are represented in Britain and western Europe.

Dragonflies are able to reproduce in almost ny kind of fresh water that is not too hot,

acid or saline. They inhabit watercourses throughout their length, from highland streams to placid, mature rivers in the plains. There are species adapted to breeding in temporary ponds, rockpools, waterfalls, brackish marshes, and even the water that collects in the leaf-bases of certain forest plants. In Hawaii lives the only species known to have a terrestrial larva, *Mega-lagrion oahuense*. It inhabits leaf litter on the forest floor and its closest relatives live in forest streams from which their larvae occasionally wander.

Classification. The order Odonata is repre-sented today by three suborders: Zygoptera, Anisoptera and Anisozygoptera. All but two of the 5,000 or so known species belong to the first two suborders.

Zygoptera, known as damselflies, have both pairs of wings similar in shape and stem-like at the base. The compound eyes are widely separated and project like buttons on either side of the head. The male has four caudal appendages, two above and two below, and the female ovipositor is always well developed. The larvae have external gills at the tip or sides of the abdomen. Zygoptera are delicate, weakly flying dragonflies com-prising 17 families, one of which is extinct.

In Anisoptera the hindwings are much broader than the forewings, neither pair being

stem-like at the base. The compound eyes are always less than one eye-width apart and usually touch across the middle of the head. The male has only three caudal appendages, two above and one below. The ovipositor may be well developed (Aeshnidae and Petaluridae) or reduced (Libellulidae, Cordu-liidae, Gomphidae). The larvae have gills inside the rectum and the anus is closed by three spines. Anisoptera are robust, strongly flying insects, second to none in aerial agility. Some migrate regularly and have been known to accomplish flights of hundreds of miles over the sea. There are eight living families.

Anisozygoptera possess characters inter-mediate between those of Zygoptera and Anisoptera, although the larvae more closely resemble Anisoptera. The suborder is known from 11 families, all of which are extinct except one, the Epiophlebiidae, represented by two very similar species inhabiting upland streams in Japan and Nepal.

Odonata have an unusually long and rich fossil history, which shows them to be the most archaic and isolated of winged insects. The earliest known Odonata occurred in the Upper Carboniferous era, about 280 million years ago, and included the largest known insect, *Meganeura monyi*, which had a wing-span of 28 in (70 cm) against the $7\frac{1}{2}$ in (19 cm) of the largest living dragonfly.

Adult dragonflies lay eggs in or near water. The aquatic larva casts its skin 8–15 times before completing development. At the end of the last stage the adult organs begin to form inside the larval skin. The first of these six pictures of the male *Aeshna cyanea* shows this stage, the nymph in water. It then climbs out of the water (second picture), hatches (third picture) and the adult dragonfly wriggles free of the nymphal skin, then hangs clinging to it while its wings expand, harden and dry. Only then is it ready to take wing.

Morphology. In basic structure the larvae and adults of dragonflies do not differ greatly. Nevertheless, the aquatic larva and flight-oriented adult each has features that reflect their different modes of life.

The adults of all species are immediately recognizable as dragonflies by the characters mentioned at the beginning of this article. The large sloping thorax accommodates the powerful flight muscles and orientates the legs forward so that they can readily grasp the prey which is usually captured on the wing. Some migratory Anisoptera have a very broad base to the hindwing that enables them to glide. Where the head is attached to the thorax, it engages with tufts of fine bristles that serve as a gravitational sensing device enabling equilibrium to be preserved in flight. The large compound eyes have lenses (facets) of two kinds: those on the upper surface are small and very responsive to movement, while those below are larger and perceive shapes. The eyes perform a major function when adults are feeding, or interacting with other dragonflies, in flight. In certain tropical Aeshnidae that feed mainly at twilight the compound eyes occupy almost the whole surface of the head.

Dragonflies mate in a manner that is unique among insects and their structure and behaviour are modified accordingly. Although the gonads and genital opening of the male are in the usual position, at the tip of the abdomen, the intromittent organ (penis) and accessory claspers are at the base of the abdomen, on the ventral surface of the second and third segments. The female genital opening is in the usual position, at the tip of the abdomen. Mating begins by the male grasping the female's head (in Anisoptera) or prothorax (in Zygoptera) with his caudal appendages, which are often specially shaped so as to interlock with corresponding depression on the female's body. Attached thus, a male and female are said to be 'in tandem'. The male, by movements of his abdomen, then encourages the female to bend the tip of her abdomen downwards and forwards so as to engage with his accessory genitalia to which he had previously transferred a sperm capsule. When the female's genitalia join those of the male a 'copulation wheel' is formed. All Odonata mate in this way.

Larval structure reflects the demands of the aquatic environment, especially with regard to breathing, locomotion and feeding. Like the adult, the larva has an internal system of strengthened tubes (tracheae) that carry oxygen to the tissues. However, in the larva this oxygen is replenished, not through open spiracles, but by diffusion through gills. In most Zygoptera these gills are three leaf-like plates (caudal lamellae) borne on the tip of the abdomen. A few Zygoptera also have filamentous gills projecting from the sides of the abdomen, similar to those of mayflies or alderflies. In most Anisoptera the gills line the inside wall of the hind-gut and are ventilated by water being pumped in and out

of the abdomen. A muscular diaphragm across the middle of the abdomen assists in this process. The respiratory devices are employed also as an emergency means of locomotion, the Anisoptera larva using the diaphragm to achieve a kind of jet propulsion.

Dragonfly larvae catch their prey in an unusual way. Typically, they remain motionless until a small creature comes near enough to be detected by sight or touch. When the creature comes within range, the larva suddenly extends the labium, at the tip of which are hooks that open to grasp the prey. The labium then draws the victim back to the mandibles. When in the resting position, the labium lies folded beneath the head and thorax, sometimes hiding the lower part of the face; for this reason it is sometimes called the 'mask'. The sudden extension of the labium is the result of a localized increase in blood pressure, a condition controlled by the abdominal diaphragm.

The shape, colour and behaviour of dragonfly larvae depend on the micro-environment they occupy. For example, mud-burrowers tend to be hairy, dark and sluggish, whereas those living amongst plants near the surface are usually smooth, pale and lively.

Breeding. Adult dragonflies lay eggs in or near water. The aquatic larva casts its skin 8–15 times before completing development, passing through a corresponding number of intervening stages, or instars. The first instar (prolarva) is unlike the others in appearance and duration. It somewhat resembles the pupa of a wasp or beetle, the functionless appendages lying closely against the body. A few minutes after leaving the egg it moults to disclose the spider-like second-instar larva usually about $\frac{1}{25}$ in (1 mm) long. From this

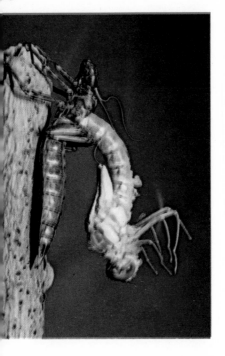

age on, the larva feeds actively on small
ater animals such as Protozoa and minute
rustacea and, later, beetles, mosquito
rvae and even small fishes. At an early stage
ing buds appear on the larva's body, and
ese become larger at each subsequent
oult. There is no pupal stage. Near the end
f the last instar the adult organs begin to
orm inside the larval skin. When these
ternal changes have been completed, the
rva climbs out of the water and moults to
isclose the adult, a process known as
mergence'. This whole process, from
aving the water to being ready to fly, may
ke only 20 min in the tropics but several
ours in temperate latitudes. As a rule, larger
ragonflies leave the water after sunset and
ke to flight just before sunrise, so their
mergence is seldom witnessed by man.
maller species may be seen emerging during
e daytime.

The newly emerged dragonfly is a pale, soft
reature with glistening wings. Its first flight
kes it away from water and it spends the
ext few days (2–15 depending on the species
nd weather) feeding actively. During this
me it is developing its full colouration and
ecoming sexually mature. When this
aturation period is over, the adult seeks
ater and enters the reproductive period,
hich may last up to six weeks. During the
eproductive period males assemble at the
ating site, usually the pond or river where
e eggs will be laid, and soon space
emselves out along the shore, each coming
defend a well defined area, or 'territory'. In
veral respects this activity resembles the
warming of other insects (e.g. mayflies and
osquitoes), the main difference being that
djacent dragonflies are further apart. Large
ecies have larger territories than do small

species, but the size of territory tends to
remain constant within a species.

Mature males compete actively, by displaying and fighting, for occupancy of territories and so, as in birds, it is the most
vigorous individuals that retain possession.
When a female flies near a territory the
resident male tries to mate with her. In some
species a courtship display precedes mating.
The male of *Calopteryx virgo*, for example,
hovers in front of the female who, by her
responses, accepts or rejects his suit. More
often, however, there is no evident courtship
and mating occurs without delay, the pair
usually flying away from water to settle while
in the mating embrace.

After transfer of the sperm capsule has
been completed, the female lays eggs either
immediately or after a delay. If laying
immediately, she may do so alone, with the
male still holding her in the tandem position,
or with him hovering nearby, darting at other
males that approach her.

Eggs are laid in one of two ways. Species
having a well developed ovipositor place them
in or amongst plant tissue, above or below the
water. Some (e.g. *Erythromma, Lestes*)
regularly climb 1 ft (30 cm) or more below the
surface and may remain submerged for at
least an hour. Species without an ovipositor
wash the eggs off the tip of the abdomen, by
dipping it into the water as they fly over it, or
drop them onto the surface. Those inhabiting
running water often lay eggs equipped with
adhesive or anchoring devices. Those breeding in waterfalls may stick the eggs onto
moist rocks in the spray zone.

Weather permitting, adult dragonflies continue to feed and to visit the breeding site
throughout life.

Habits. The basic life-history is the same in all

dragonflies, but the duration and timing of the
different stages vary considerably according
to the restrictions imposed by climate.

To reproduce, a dragonfly needs warmth
and water in which to lay its eggs. Where both
these requirements are continuously satisfied
(as in permanent waters in the tropics)
breeding is uninterrupted. Where there is
regularly a cold or dry season, the dragonfly
life-history is specially modified to include a
stage adapted to survive the unfavourable
period.

Where a cold season interrupts reproduction every year (as in temperate latitudes)
the winter is passed in a resistant stage.
Occasionally this is the immature adult, as in
Sympecma fusca, a small damselfly of continental Europe. In some genera (e.g. *Lestes,
Aeshna*) it is the egg that hibernates, but
usually it is the larva. Depending on the
species and location, the life-history in
northern temperate regions (Europe and
North America) may take one to five years. In
southern Europe a few species (e.g. *Ischnura
elegans*) can complete two generations a year.
In temperate regions most species are
adapted to emerge at a particular time of
year. So there are species characteristic of
spring (e.g. *Pyrrhosoma, Anax, Brachytron*)
and others characteristic of summer
(*Coenagrion, Aeshna, Sympetrum*). The position of the flying season is maintained by the
larvae responding in a specific way to factors
such as temperature and daylength.

Where a dry season interrupts reproduction (as in seasonal rainfall areas in the
tropics) the adult provides the resistant stage.
In some genera (e.g. *Lestes, Gynacantha*) the
adult remains in the protection of the forest,
while in others (e.g. *Pantala, Tramea*) it
migrates continually, flying by day and

resting by night, following the moving rain-belt, and laying eggs in the temporary pools that appear along its path. In both these kinds of life-history only one to three months are needed to complete the combined egg and larval stages. CLASS: Insecta, PHYLUM: Arthropoda.   P.S.C.

DRILL *Mandrillus leucophaeus,* a baboon closely related to the mandrill. See baboon.

DRIVE, the impression we get that an animal is impelled by something within, as when, in seeking food, it continues to search until food is found. This sense of being driven gave rise to the concept of 'drive' as an inner com-pulsive force motivating behaviour. The hypothesis of 'drive' attempts to explain the spontaneity of some behaviour, the fluctua-tions in the level of response in an individual and the persistent or 'go-seeking' nature of behaviour, a persistence which may remain even when the stimulus evoking the behaviour is removed, so that the animal searches until it finds the stimulus object once again. It also attempts to explain the grouping of some activities so that they are all evoked together, such as all the activities concerned with reproduction. Attempts have been made to catalogue the number of drives which an animal may display. A method used with rats has been to place a hungry rat in a box connected to another box by a corridor. On the floor of the corridor was a metal grid through which an electric current could be passed. Food was put in the second box and the rat tried to cross the grid to reach it. Then the strength of the current required to prevent the animal going along the corridor was measured. Similar measurements were made with thirsty rats going to water, male rats attracted by a female on heat and so forth. It was even found that a measurable current had to be used to prevent a rat from going to an empty box, so there appeared to be a drive for exploration.

This attempt to rank the drives in an order of their strength is, however, open to much criticism.

For example, the existence of a drive is purely hypothetical, and is inferred from observed behaviour. It is, however, also possible to offer an explanation in physio-logical terms. An active animal, for example, uses up blood sugar to provide energy for its muscular movement. This comes from stores in its liver and, more directly, from food in its gut. If it has gone unfed for a period the level of blood sugar will have dropped and this reduced level will affect areas in the brain. Artificial stimulation of these areas will, however, initiate the *appetitive behaviour by which the animal seeks food, an activity which gives all the indications of being the result of a 'hunger drive'.

Hormones, too, produce their behavioural

effects by arousing the animal and initiating certain behaviour. The changes in day-length in late winter and early spring bring about changes in the gonads of male birds and the hormones which circulate as a result cause a male to set up a territory and defend it against other males. The male is then said to show a reproductive drive.

It is not always necessary that drive should be attached to one particular kind of be-haviour. States of 'general drive' appear to exist which concern the total activity of the animal.

When behaviour begins to be less intense or there is a reduction in the readiness with which the behaviour can be invoked one can talk conveniently of a drive reduction. Some comparative psychologists have considered reward in a learning situation as having its effect by drive reduction but this argument leads in a circle. Thus, the act is done because it brings drive reduction, yet drive reduction occurs because the act has been done.   J.D.C.

DROMEDARY, name for a special slender breed of Arabian or One-humped camel *Camelus dromedarius,* used for riding but often and erroneously used for any individual of that species. See camel.

DRONGOS, a family of medium-size arboreal songbirds with flycatcher-like habits. There are 20 species, showing relativ similarity. They occur through Africa sout of the Sahara, southern Asia from India t China, and south to Australasia. They var from 7–15 in (18–38 cm) in length but this due in part to a fairly long tail. Elaborate lon outer tail feathers may, in some specie nearly double this length. Drongos show th typical modifications that occur in flycatch ing birds. The stance on a perch is upright, th legs are short, the wing long and tapering, an the tail well-developed and forked. The bill strong and stout, hooked at the tip an slightly notched to grip the prey, with lon strong bristles around the base. Drongos a agile and swift in flight and can manoeuvr quickly. The feet are strong and can not onl help to seize larger prey in the air but can als be used to hold an insect and raise it towar the bill parrot fashion.

The plumage is grey in two species, fligl feathers are red-brown in another, but othe wise drongos are black, with a few showin some white on the underside, wing-coverts head. The black plumage shows glosses blue green or purple to varying degrees, ofte confined to a part of the plumage. On som

Black drongo or King crow *Dicrurus macrocercus,* stoops like a falcon at predators attacking its nest.

Flock of teal or Dabbling ducks with two Spotted redshanks in front and Common shelduck on the water.

such as the Spangled drongo *Dicrurus hot-entottus* the gloss is limited to spots at the feather tips. The tips of the forked tail may be greatly extended, apparently as a decoration, and this may vary between forms of the same species living on different islands. Rarely the outer pair of feathers are long, curved, bare barbs ending in racquets. Some birds show crests, varying in different species from small forehead tufts to full curly crests.

The drongos are usually solitary, perching on some vantage point from which they can fly out or swoop to catch their prey in flycatcher or roller fashion. They feed mainly on insects, although on some occasions they may take some nectar. They are inquisitive and quick to investigate any distubance. They are also very aggressive and will readily attack birds of prey or crows larger than themselves, but do not appear to harm smaller birds, which may nest near a drongo's nest, apparently for protection.

The nests are frail-looking, shallow cups suspended in forked twigs usually well up in trees. They are made of thin, flexible stems and roots, and bound together with spider's webs. The two to four eggs vary from white to buff or pink; variably spotted, blotched or, rarely, streaked with brown, red or black. The female alone incubates but the naked nestlings are cared for by both parents.

The calls of drongos are very varied, consisting of whistling, chuckling, harsh or melodious notes. The song-phrases are usually brief. Some species are mimics, especially of whistling calls. FAMILY: Dicruridae, ORDER: Passeriformes, CLASS: Aves.

DRUMFISHES, an alternative name for croakers.

DUCKBILL *Ornithorhynchus anatinus,* the Australian egg-laying mammal more commonly referred to today as *platypus.

DUCKS, aquatic birds comprising most of the smaller members of the family Anatidae which also contains the geese and swans. There are 147 species of birds in the family, most of which are ducks. Within the limits of the restrictions imposed upon them by their aquatic mode of life the ducks vary widely in forms and habits, much more widely than their goose and swan relatives. The family is divided into ten tribes, on the basis of various physical and behavioural characteristics, and eight of these tribes are composed entirely, or largely, of species to which the name 'duck' is commonly applied. The tribes, with their arrangement in three subfamilies, are as follows. In the subfamily Anseranatinae is the single tribe Anseranatini containing the one species of Magpie goose *Anseranas semipalmata* of Australia and New Guinea.

In the subfamily Anserinae there are two tribes: the Dendrocygnini containing the eight species of Whistling ducks or Tree ducks; and the Anserini containing the six species of swans and the 15 species of true geese. The subfamily Anatinae contains the other seven tribes and the rest of the species. The tribes are: Tadornini, shelducks and sheldgeese; Anatini, Dabbling ducks; Aythyini, pochards; Cairinini, Perching ducks and Perching geese; Somateriini, eiders; Mergini, scoters, mergansers and goldeneyes; and Oxyurini, stifftails.

The swans and geese have their own entries and therefore only the Whistling ducks and the ducks in the various tribes of Anatinae are dealt with below. Of these the best-known, and probably the most characteristic and basic forms are the species of Dabbling ducks of the tribe Anatini. These are the types most commonly regarded as 'ducks' in popular terminology and this is the group from which most of the world's domesticated ducks have been derived.

The term 'duck' has a somewhat variable usage. It may be used for any of the species of ducks so far mentioned, but also it may refer to the female only of any of these species: thus 'mallard duck' as distinct from 'mallard drake'—the latter of course being the male. Also the term may be used as a plural 'several duck' for example. The

Ducks

Swimming ducks rise vertically from the water; diving ducks must patter on the surface to become airborne.

American usage of the term 'hen' for the female duck is obviously sound.

The more common ducks of ponds and lakes are well known, but several groups have taken advantage of the food supply which is available beneath the surface of these waters. The Dabbling ducks can only reach food in shallow water, but the stifftails, the mergansers, the pochards and, to a certain extent, the eiders feed largely beneath the surface. The mergansers, and particularly the eiders, also feed in salt waters, diving for fishes, or shellfishes respectively. Certain forms, such as the goldeneyes and Harlequin duck, feed largely in fast-flowing streams in the Arctic, and the Torrent ducks—usually regarded as aberrant Dabbling ducks but perhaps more properly placed with the Perching ducks—are at home in the apparently impossibly fast torrents of South American streams and rapids.

The Whistling ducks and the Perching ducks commonly perch in trees and, like the goldeneyes and the buffleheads, even nest in trees, usually in holes. The shelducks nest in holes in the ground and some species, including the ubiquitous mallard, nest in a variety of situations, on or off the ground. The redhead (a pochard) and the Black-headed duck (a stifftail) are brood parasites laying their eggs in the nests of other species of birds—not only ducks.

Most ducks, particularly those that dive,

are less efficient at locomotion on land than in the water, but some species, especially the smaller ones, are quite efficient walkers. The Whistling ducks are in fact quite at home on land. They have longer legs than other ducks and have a remarkable range of locomotor abilities, flying, walking, perching and swimming at or beneath the surface with almost equal facility.

The size variation in ducks is considerable, as is illustrated by two South American species: the Muscovy duck, the male of which is some 30 in (76 cm) long, and the Ringed teal, about a third of that length and a much smaller fraction of the bulk. And the plumage variation is remarkable; in some species both sexes are dull, and without plumes, crests, wing patches or other ornaments. In others, such as the Mandarin duck and the Carolina duck, the male has a magnificent plumage of bright colours and patterns, with a crest on the head; and the Mandarin in addition has a pair of feather 'sails' on the back. Other species have greatly elongated tail feathers, while others again are particularly striking for the beauty of colour, pattern and design of their plumage.

The eight species of the Whistling duck tribe together have a world-wide distribution, except for Europe. One species, the Fulvous whistling duck *Dendrocygna bicolor* is found in South and Central America, East Africa, and Madagascar, India, Burma and Ceylon, without any noticeable geographical variation of form. The Wandering whistling duck *Dendrocygna arcuata,* on the other hand, is found in three forms—in the East Indies, in tropical Australia and New Guinea and in New Britain—and the Red-billed whistling duck *Dendrocygna autumnalis,*

found from the southern United States southwards into South America, is divided into northern and southern forms. The various forms of these two species tend to interbreed where they overlap.

The Whistling duck found most commonly in zoological collections is probably the White-faced whistling duck *Dendrocygna viduata* native to tropical South America and also southern Africa, Madagascar and the Comoro Islands. Eyton's whistling duck *Dendrocygna eytoni* of Australia and Tasmania is a striking bird having pale-coloured plumes extending backwards from the lower breast and flank region on each side. The Spotted whistling duck *Dendrocygna guttata* is found in the East Indies and the Black-billed whistling duck *Dendrocygna arborea* in the West Indies. The Lesser whistling duck *Dendrocygna javanica* inhabits a large part of Asia southwards and eastwards from India.

In addition to their long legs the Whistling ducks have physical features which give them the appearance more of a goose than a duck. Like geese but unlike the 'true' ducks of the subfamily Anatinae, they do not show pronounced sexual dimorphism. Such structural features, together with behavioural characters, such as the nature of their breeding displays and the shared parental care, have resulted in the Whistling ducks being classified with the geese and swans.

Of the seven tribes of 'true' ducks by far the most common and successful is the tribe Anatini containing those species variously known as 'Dabbling ducks', 'River ducks' or 'Surface-feeding ducks'. Birds of this group do not dive, except in unusual circumstances, but obtain all their food at or near the surface of the water or on damp ground or

The Cape teal *Anas capensis* ranges from Lake Chad southwards to Bechuanaland.

Mallard, the commonest duck, ancestor of the farmyard duck, ranges over most of the northern hemisphere.

vegetation. This food may include a wide variety of edible materials, both plant and animal. Most of the species of this tribe are birds of fresh water, though a few may nest near the sea shore and a number regularly pass over the sea during migration. These migrations may be very extensive, totalling a few thousands of miles in some species.

The arrangement of the Anatini is principally into 14 different groups, many of which have at some time been given separate generic names but which are all now classified in the single genus *Anas*. 39 species are now generally recognized. These include such apparently diverse forms as the mallard *A. platyrhynchos*, the shoveler *A. clypeata*, the wigeon *A. penelope*, the Green-winged teal *A. crecca* and the pintail *A. acuta*. Externally these species seem to be very different from one another, but their behaviour and internal structure shows that they are in fact closely related. Five other, rather aberrant, forms are often included in this tribe. One of these is the Ringed teal *Calonetta leucophrys*, already mentioned, which may in fact be more properly placed in the Perching duck tribe.

Nearly half the Dabbling duck species show a strong sexual dimorphism, the male being brightly coloured and the female dull and cryptic. This dimorphism is, as is usual in birds, connected with the breeding display

of the male and the female's need for concealment, particularly while on the nest. Most of the other species are dull coloured, in both sexes, but a few, such as the Chiloe wigeon *A. sibilatrix,* have bright plumage in both sexes. All Dabbling ducks have two moults per year, which ensure the replacement of worn or damaged feathers. In the sexually dimorphic species the bright breeding plumage of the male is replaced, in the post-breeding moult, by an 'eclipse' plumage similar to that of the female.

A further outstanding plumage feature of the Dabbling ducks is the presence of a brightly coloured patch of feathers on the wing. This is called the speculum and is seen in both sexes. Usually it involves the secondary wing feathers only, but other adjacent areas of feathering may play a part. Most specula are in metallic shades of green or blue, often combined with patches or stripes of white, and are very striking, although they may not be visible when the wing is folded. It is thought that the role of the speculum is one of communication within the species. Different species have different specula and the display of the speculum plays an important part in the courtship ceremonies, probably helping to ensure mating between birds of the same species. It may also assist in the co-ordination of movements of bird flocks engaged in complex flight manoeuvres, being

a plainly visible feature of every extended wing.

The connection between bright plumage and breeding display is well shown in the Dabbling ducks, the more brightly coloured species on the whole having the more elaborate display. The display of the mallard drake is fairly typical for the group. As the breeding season approaches the drakes build up the variety and intensity of their display movements and calls, performing both to females and, socially, to males. The more outstanding components of the display are as follows. After a considerable amount of mock preening, mock drinking and preliminary shaking the drake will perform one or more of the movements called 'grunt-whistle', 'head-up-tail-up' and 'down-up'. In the grunt-whistle the bird bends forwards, placing its bill in the water and then it arches the body up before withdrawing the bill while shaking the head. The shaking of the bill in the water before it is withdrawn results in an arc of water droplets being thrown up. Also, as the bird performs the movement it emits a distinctive short whistle followed by a distinct grunt. The head-up-tail-up is the most complicated of the displays. Both head and tail are drawn rapidly upwards while the bird remains sitting on the water and as they are also moved towards each other the bird's profile is much altered. At the same time the

White domesticated Muscovy ducks, fairly common farm birds, particularly in America. They derive from the wild muscovy which is greenish with red wattles.

'elbows' are raised to reveal both the speculum and the curled feathers of the rump, both distinctive features of the mallard drake. The bird also emits a loud whistle simultaneously. The whole display takes about a second. The down-up is much simpler and seems like a very exaggerated and speeded-up drinking movement. The bird dips its bill down into the water while tipping forward and then brings it up so fast that a spurt of water is lifted from the surface while the breast is still down and the tail up. At this climax point a whistle is emitted.

Such complex performances, given by every normal male during the breeding season, must have some definite function and detailed comparative studies indicate that this involves not only the stimulation of the performer and of his mate, but also, because of differences in different species, the display is a means of ensuring recognition of the performer's species, therefore preventing breeding between closely related species.

The mallard group of species includes not only the well-known Mallard duck itself which, in various races, breeds across most of the northern half of the world and has given rise to most of the domesticated forms of duck, but also several other species including the North American black duck *A. rubripes*, the Philippine duck *A. luzonica*, various races of spotbill *A. poecilorhyncha* in Asia and of yellowbill *A. undulata* in Africa. The Hawaiian duck *A. wyvilliana* and the Laysan teal *A. laysanensis* are island forms which survive only in very small numbers.

The aberrant species of Dabbling ducks, in addition to the Ringed teal, are the New Zealand Blue duck *Hymenolaimus malacorhynchos*, which has a peculiar bill apparently adapted for sucking algae off the stones in the remote streams where it lives; the Pink-eared duck *Malacorhynchus membranaceus*, of Australia, which has a long bill

The South African or Cape shelduck *Tadorna cana*.

with flaps at the tip, also for feeding or algae; the Freckled duck *Stictonetta naevosa*, also of Australia but rare; and the Pink-headed duck *Rhodonessa caryophyllacea* which is now probably extinct but was formerly found in north and eastern India and adjacent countries.

The Dabbling ducks are significant in that they form the bulk of the quarry of wild-fowlers and other duck-hunters. The next most important group in this respect is the tribe of freshwater diving ducks, the Aythyini, most of which are called pochards. In North America the canvasback *Aythya valisineria* is a favourite quarry as is the redhead *A. americana*. These birds are basically grey on the body, black on the tail and upper breast and chestnut brown on the head in the male; the female being brown. The canvasback has a longer bill and is a paler grey. The European pochard *A. ferina* has the body shape of the redhead but in colouration and head shape is intermediate between the other two species.

Also in the genus *Aythya* are the four species of white-eye which are basically brown above and paler below in both sexes. *A. innotata* is found in Madagascar, *A. nyroca* in Eurasia, *A. baeri* in east Asia and *A. australis* in Australasia. The best known species of the genus in Europe is probably the Tufted duck *A. fuligula*, which breeds across Europe and Asia from Iceland to the Pacific. The drake is black above and white beneath, with a pendant crest from the back of his head. The female is brown with a hint of crest. This duck is common not only on natural fresh waters but also on artificial lakes and reservoirs in both town and country and becomes very tame. A fairly close relative is the ring-neck *A. collaris* of North and Central America.

The food of most members of the Aythyini is largely vegetable, but the scaups take a larger proportion of animal food. The Greater scaup *A. marila* is the sturdiest species and spends more time on the sea than the others. It ranges across the whole of the northern hemisphere. The Lesser scaup *A. affinis* is restricted to America. The scaup males are grey-bodied with black rump and breast. The head and neck are basically black also but the Greater scaup has a green sheen on the head and the Lesser is more purple. In America the scaups are also known as bluebills.

The pochard most commonly kept in captivity is the Red-crested pochard *Netta rufina*, the male of which has a striking plumage of black, pale grey and brown, with a light chestnut head and orange bill. It breeds sporadically in Europe but principally in western Asia. The rosybill *N. peposaca* is a striking South American pochard, with a black-purple and grey plumage and a knobbed red bill.

The perching ducks and geese, tribe Cairinini, are somewhat peculiar species which spend more time in trees than other ducks. They vary considerably in form, size and plumage-pattern, from the tiny Pygmy geese of the genus *Nettapus* of which there are three species in Africa, southern Asia and Australia, to the very large, 32 in (81 cm), Spur-winged goose *Plectropterus gambensis* of Africa. Two species of Perching ducks are very well known in aviculture: the mandarin *Aix galericulata* of eastern Asia (also breeding as an escape in Britain) and the Carolina or Wood duck *Aix sponsa* of the eastern half of the United States and southern Canada. In each species the male has a striking multi-coloured plumage, including a very handsome backward-sweeping crest. In the mandarin this crest is erectile and there is also a pair of 'sails' on the back formed from a specially modified pair of chestnut coloured feathers. There is strong sexual dimorphism in these two species, though this is not the case for other members of the tribe.

A further noteworthy species of the Perching duck group is the muscovy *Cairina moschata*, the ancestor of the domestic muscovy which is a fairly common farm bird, particularly in America, although not as successful in domestication as the mallard. The wild muscovy is a large irides-

Eider drake, feeds on crabs and shellfish.

Pintail drake, a shy duck that quickly takes to the wing.
Hottentot teal *Anas punctata* on Lake Nakuru. The species ranges from Uganda to Cape Province.

cent black bird which breeds in Mexico, Central and South America.

The tribe Tadornini contains the shelduck and sheldgeese which, though resembling geese in general form are more closely related to the Dabbling ducks. In this tribe both species are brightly coloured, though sometimes differently, and in the majority of species there is a metallic wing speculum. Basically the tribe is divided into the shelducks of the genus *Tadorna*, ranging across Europe, Africa, Asia and Australasia, and the sheldgeese, genus *Clöephaga*, found only in South America.

The Common shelduck *T. tadorna* breeds from the coasts of western Europe eastwards through much of central Asia, nesting usually in burrows in the ground. It has striking white, green-black and chestnut plumage, with red bill and legs. The sexes are similar although the female is smaller. In the sheldgeese of South America, which are larger and more goose-like, some, such as the Ashy-headed goose *Clöephaga poliocephala*, have similar sexes, while in others, such as the Magellan goose *C. picta*, the female is basically brown and the male white.

Aberrant members of the Tadornini include the Steamer ducks, genus *Tachyeres*, of South America and the Falkland Islands. These are large, powerfully-swimming ducks

The mandarin, most showy of ornamental ducks.

of three species, two of which are flightless.

The tribe Mergini, the Sea ducks, contains a variety of species which obtain their food by diving in both fresh and salt waters. They include the sawbills, or mergansers, of the genus *Mergus,* which have serrated bills for holding slippery fishes; the scoters, genus *Melanitta,* which are bulky and black and dive for shellfishes which are crushed in the especially muscular gizzard; the goldeneyes, genus *Clangula,* which nest in holes in trees, as do some of the mergansers to which they are closely related; and the harlequin and Old squaw. The last two are striking arctic species, the harlequin *Histrionicus histrionicus,* having a boldly marked blue, white and chestnut plumage and inhabiting fast-flowing streams, and the Old squaw or Long-tailed duck *Clangula hyemalis,* having two different plumages, both basically black and white, one winter and one summer. The females are cryptically coloured.

Until recently the eiders were also included in the tribe Mergini but are now generally placed in a tribe of their own, the Somateriini. There are four species of eider, three of them in the genus *Somateria.* The Common eider *S. mollissima* has provided man with the best down for pillows and mattresses and this important species has its own entry. Female eiders, like all the female Mergini, are cryptic, but the males are boldly marked in black and white and, in *Somateria,* have apple or emerald green on the head. Steller's eider *Polysticta stelleri* is smaller than the other species and the male has a chestnut breast and belly. The male King eider *S. spectabilis* is an outstandingly handsome bird with soft grey on the head as

Shoveler duck scoops small items of food from surface of water with its broad bill.

well as green, and with an unusual helmeted forehead formed from a continuation of the orange horn of the bill.

Finally, the tribe of stifftails, Oxyurini, contains a number of dumpy little fresh-water diving ducks most of which are red-brown in colour with blue bills. It includes the Ruddy duck *Oxyura jamaicensis,* which breeds, as a number of subspecies, from North to South America and another South American species, the Black-headed duck *Heteronetta atricapilla,* which is parasitic, laying its eggs in the nests of other species of birds. FAMILY: Anatidae, ORDER: Anseriformes, CLASS: Aves. P.M.D.

DUGONG *Dugong dugon,* a large, totally aquatic, herbivorous mammal which lives in warm Indo-Pacific seas. There is one species only, which comprises one of the three genera of modern Sirenia or seacows. The other genera are the manatee of the Atlantic and the extinct Steller's seacow of the North Pacific. Some claim to distinguish an eastern and a western form of the dugong.

The dugong commonly grows to a length of about 10 ft (3 m) although lengths of 16 ft (5 m) have been noted. It is a heavily built animal of torpedo-shape with a horizontally flattened whale-like tail. Like the whales, too, all trace of hindlegs has disappeared in the course of evolutionary adaptation to aquatic life. The fore flippers are small and take no part in propulsion. All the bones are of exceptional density and the skull is heavy and down-turned in front. The teeth are limited to a small number of crushing teeth and there are horny pads in the front of each jaw. The young have five or six cusped molars on each side of each jaw, and these teeth fall out progressively from the front so that only two may remain in the adult. A pair of tusks is also present in the upper jaw which, in the male, protrudes without known

function. The tusks of the female never become visible.

The grey skin is of immense thickness and toughness but there is no substantial blubber layer beneath. The skin is nearly hairless but has individual hairs about $\frac{1}{4}$ in (7 mm) long and about 2–3 in (5–8 cm) apart. By tradition it was a dugong skin which protected the Ark of the Covenant during the wanderings in the wilderness. The flesh is palatable, and oil may be rendered particularly from the head and forward part of the body.

The head is well suited to feeding on plants growing on the bottom. The bristly mask forms a flat and down-turned front to the head above the mouth. The nostrils are high on the head and, in adaptation to taking air from the surface, are equipped with powerful muscular valves. The eyes are small and circular and the minute ear holes are only to be found by careful scrutiny.

The single pair of mammary glands are pectoral in position, almost in the armpit as it were. The occasional suckling of a young one held vertically by a flipper must be one of the reasons for the mermaid myth.

The dugong is limited in its distribution to the coastal waters of warm seas from the Solomon Islands in the east to the head of the Red Sea in the west. It extends north to the Philippine Islands and the Persian Gulf and south to Brisbane, Perth and almost to Mozambique. However, today its numbers have been greatly depleted by man almost everywhere so that it has become a rare animal. On the east coast of Australia there was systematic exploitation for oil, in the last century by the European Australians, in addition to local hunting. The only areas where the dugong stock is still substantial seems to be the far northeastern region of Australia and the Torres Straits.

The fact that it lives almost continuously submerged under water makes the dugong

quite exceptionally difficult of study. Breathing at the surface is normally a brief soundless visit every few minutes, the tips of the nostrils only just becoming visible. But it can be asserted that the period of gestation is long, that one young is normally born at a time and that it probably accompanies its mother for a considerable period. Dugongs tend to live in groups and at times may be highly gregarious. Enormous herds moving together were recorded in Moreton Bay off Brisbane early in the last century. No evidence exists of regular migrations nor of movements across deep waters.

Their habit is to feed, especially at night, in the shallow areas where dense patches of dugong grass (*Zostera* etc.) grow. The food is pulled off by the powerful lips, and it is dislodged vegetation floating to the surface which commonly informs the hunter of the creature's presence. Hunting primitively is by harpoon or nets. Dugongs are extremely sensitive to sound or disturbance of the water and that attribute is their chief protection. FAMILY: Dugongidae, ORDER: Sirenia, CLASS: Mammalia.   C.K.B. and G.C.L.B.

DUIKER, a group of small African antelopes of uncertain affinities. None is more than 30 in (76 cm) tall and many species are less than half that height. The head is conical with a convex nose and a small bare muzzle. The horns are smooth, somewhat keeled, and placed on a backwardly-projecting eminence of the frontal bone. In front of the eyes are face-glands, which are quite different both in position and structure to those of other bovids. Instead of being close to the eye, they are halfway between it and the muzzle. There is a line of bare skin, lying at a slight angle to the eye-muzzle axis, which is studded with a line of glandular pores. As well as face-glands, duikers have foot-glands, and sometimes inguinal (groin) glands too. The duiker's fur is short and close, often rather harsh and longer on the rump than on the neck, and there is usually a long tuft between the horns.

Duikers occur all over subsaharan Africa. They inhabit both forest and savannah, but even the savannah forms are found mostly in places with thick ground-cover. There is only one savannah species in the genus *Sylvicapra*; this has long legs, and the horns turn upwards from the base. On the other hand there are at least 11 species of the forest duikers, genus *Cephalophus*. Although it is true that some of these live on the forest edge and even in bush country, it is strikingly illustrative of the variety of habitats offered by the forest and the corresponding paucity of savannah niches. Forest duikers have horns that point straight backwards in a line with the face, and their build is wedge-shaped, with short forelegs and a high rounded rump—an obvious adaptation to

pushing through thick undergrowth. The name comes from the Afrikaans word meaning 'diver', referring to the way duikers plunge into the undergrowth when disturbed.

The forest duikers have been classified in various ways. Formerly it was usual to place them in two genera or subgenera according to whether they possessed inguinal glands or not, but recently it has become clear that it is not possible really to see from dried skins whether the glands are there or not. The whole animal must be examined. Inguinal glands have been found to be absent in species in which they had been claimed to be present, and vice versa, and it is even thought that there may be individual variation. The best way to divide the forest duikers into species-groups is probably by size.

1. Large duikers, 29–31 in (75–80 cm)

Banded duiker or Zebra antelope of West Africa.

high, weighing 139–154 lb (63–70 kg). (a) Yellow-backed duiker *Cephalophus silvicultor*. Dark brown with a white chin and throat, and a yellow-white dorsal crest which is broad on the rump and ends in a point behind the shoulders. The hairs of the crest are erected in alarm. A thick forest species, found in lowland, montane and swamp forest, from Guinea to the Congo, Uganda, Zambia, North Angola and the Mau forest in Kenya. (b) Abbott's duiker *C. spadix*. Very similar, but slightly smaller. Chin and throat are pale, but not white; the dorsal crest is lacking. Very little is known about this species; it occurs in montane forest, from 4,500 ft (1,400 m) in Tanzania (in the northeast, and the southern highlands) and Rwanda. (c) Jentink's duiker *C. jentinki*. An extraordinarily coloured species, slightly larger than the Yellow-backed. The head and neck are black with the ear-rims, muzzle, forelimbs and a stripe over the shoulders, and hindlimbs below the hocks, white; the body is grey. It is found in thick primary forest in Liberia and the adjoining part of the Ivory Coast.

2. Medium-sized duikers, 17½–19½ in

(45–50 cm) high, weighing 33–40 lb (15–18 kg). (d) Black-fronted duiker *C. nigrifrons*. The largest of the middle group. It has big lateral hoofs, and thick horns 4 in (10 cm) long in males (only 2½ in (6 cm) in females). It is brown, with a black face-blaze and tufted tail. Found in thick forest from Cameroun to the borders of Uganda, favouring marshy forest; its broad hoofs and long lateral hoofs spread out on soft ground. It also occurs in montane forest on the Mitumba and Virunga ranges, Mts Ruwenzori, Elgon, Kenya and Kabobo. (e) Black duiker *C. niger*. Slender horns; colour black, with a reddish face-blaze. Woodland and forest margins from Sierra Leone to River Niger. (f) Black-backed duiker *C. dorsalis*. Thick horns; red-brown with a dark face-blaze and dark, diffuse dorsal stripe; white chin and throat. Found in thick forest, from Liberia to the eastern Congo. (g) Natal, Harvey's or Peters' duiker *C. natalensis*. Thick horns, only half as long, 1½ in (4 cm), in female as in male. Reddish with dark face-blaze, sometimes a trace of a dorsal stripe, white chin and throat, not a very big tail-tuft. Found in forest and bush with thick undergrowth, from the Camerouns to Uganda, the gallery forests of the Juba River (Somalia) and Tana River (Kenya), eastern Tanzania, Zanzibar, Pemba, Malawi, to Natal and eastern Transvaal. (h) Banded duiker *C. zebra*. A very distinctive type, the smallest of the middle group; horns conical, only 1¾ in (4½ cm) long in males, 1 in (2½ cm) in females. Red with 10–14 black bands across the back; chin and throat cream coloured. Found in mountain forest in Sierra Leone, Liberia and western Ivory Coast.

3. Small duikers, 12½–14 in (32–36 cm) high, weighing 13–24 lb (6–11 kg). (i) Red-flanked duiker *C. rufilatus*. Slender horns, 3 in (7.5 cm) long in males, only 1¼ in (3.5 cm) in females; reddish, darker on back and more intense on flanks; chin and throat white, tail bushy, big lateral hoofs. Found in fringing and gallery forest, forest edges, and thickets, from Senegal east to extreme northwest Uganda. (j) Blue duiker *C. monticola*. The smallest species; conical horns only 1¾ in (4½–5 cm) long in males, ¾ in (2 cm) in females; frontal tuft weak or absent; grey with a dark face-blaze, white chin and throat, and bushy tail. Found in forest with thick undergrowth, from the Niger River to the Congo, and Fernando Póo, out onto the forest edges in south Sudan and Central African Republic, and in forest-savannah mosaic and dry and montane forests in Uganda, the Kenya shores of Lake Victoria, Pemba, Mafia and Zanzibar islands, Tanzania, W. Zambia, Angola as far as 15°S, and the southeast coast of Africa to the George district, Cape Province. (k) Maxwell's duiker *C. maxwelli*. Slightly larger and browner, with a different structure to the

feet. Found in forest from the lower Niger west to Gambia, and the Bijagos islands off Portuguese Guinea.

The Bush or Grey duiker *Sylvicapra grimmia,* the only truly savannah species, has upright horns and lacks the wedge-shaped build; it is found throughout the savannah zone from South Africa to Ethiopia and Senegal.

Maxwell's duiker, the only species which has so far been well-studied, lives in pairs which are territorial. Within the territory there are two resting-places, one more favoured than the other, and places for urination and defaecation, and several marking spots, usually branches where the male is constantly rubbing secretion from his face-gland. Throughout the day and night, periods of rest alternate with bouts of restless activity, in which all parts of the territory are visited with runs and bounds; the animals sometimes making two to three jumps in one place. The territorial paths are constant and well-used. Activity is most intense in the early morning.

When alarmed, the duiker ceases its restless activity, its nervous movement, and especially its tail wagging. It stands still, its head towards the source of danger, and its ears pricked forward. The alarm call, which is understandably frequent in such nervous animals, is a shrill whistle made through the nose. When captured, Maxwell's duiker utters a sonorous bellow. When touched suddenly, the animal flexes its limbs as if going under a branch. It does not flee further than its territorial borders, attempting to hide.

The male duiker is very aggressive towards other males, and fierce fights occur when they are caged together. In zoos females tolerate others, and it is therefore possible that more than one female may belong to the same group in the wild. The male's face-glands are constantly swollen,

Buck Crowned duiker, a race of the Bush or Grey duiker, named for the tuft of hair on its head.

and he marks objects four times as frequently as the female. The intensity of marking increases when he is excited, for instance by the proximity of another male. The face-glands are also used in what Aeschlimann calls the 'accolade' ceremony, in which the male and female press their face-glands together, marking each other. The accolade is most frequent between the basic mated pair; it is rare between a male and a strange female, or between two females.

Maxwell's duiker eats grain, fruit and green leaves. It rarely drinks, most moisture being obtained from its food. While the female is urinating, the male may place his muzzle between her hindlegs where he gets sprayed. He then raises his head and draws back his upper lip, remaining still, a posture known as 'Flehmen', found in many ungulates, and usually associated with oestrus in the female, since the action aids chemoreception. The young are born in the dry season (January to March or August to September). Gestation lasts four months. Maturity is reached in three years. A single young is born, which weighs $\frac{1}{10}$ of its mother's weight. Females reproduce every year. They live ten years in captivity.

The Bush duiker seems to differ from Maxwell's in its flight reaction, being found in open country. At first, on disturbance, it squats down in the grass; if threatened it rises and makes off in a zigzag, with plunging jumps, and runs for a considerable distance. A special form of Bush duiker *Sylvicapra grimmia lobeliarum* is found among the giant lobelias and senecios of Mt Elgon, above 11,000 ft (3,350 m), isolated by forest from lowland forms. It is adapted to temperatures which may drop to freezing.

Unexpected behaviour seen among duikers is meat-eating. In captivity, where duikers are treated as pets and given their liberty, it often happens that fowls are killed by them. The duiker walks innocuously amongst them, suddenly striking with its hoofs, two together, and then eating the head and legs. Dr L. S. B. Leakey discovered that he could prevent this behaviour by giving the duiker access to salt. However, it does occur in the wild; some African hunters bait traps with meat to catch duikers.

Aeschlimann's Maxwell duikers mated at night when he could not observe it; but Frädrich describes how a male Black-backed duiker courted a female Banded duiker in Frankfurt zoo. The male was very aggressive; he followed the female around persistently until she was exhausted, and when she stood still or walked slowly, he butted her vehemently on the belly and flanks. Mating itself was not recorded. The female eats her infant's faeces; she constantly marks the young with her preorbital secretion on its head, legs and back. The secretion of Maxwell's duiker is described as a 'white rancid liquid', but that of the Banded duiker was said to be resinous, but odourless at least to man. FAMILY: Bovidae, ORDER: Artiodactyla, CLASS: Mammalia.   C.P.G.

DUNG BEETLES, dark heavy-bodied insects of the family Scarabaeidae. The name refers to their habit of feeding on animal, especially mammalian, droppings. The adults of the larger, true Dung beetles, such as *Copris* and *Canthon,* are dark brown or black with powerful spiny legs. The head often has a flat scoop-like projection used to push balls of dung over the ground. The beetles fashion the balls by breaking off a portion from a large dung mass and tumbling it to and fro until it is spherical. The beetles may also roll dung balls by holding them between their hindlegs. The spherical meal of dung is transported to a suitable retreat before being eaten. Some species of Dung beetles are unique among insects in that a male and female may co-operate in their care of the young stages. They excavate two to seven chambers in the soil and stock each with a separate store of dung. A single egg is deposited in each chamber and the female remains to guard the nest. In some species the female even remains long enough to tend her brood to maturity. The larvae develop into thick grubs with well developed legs. FAMILY: Scarabaeidae, ORDER: Coleoptera, CLASS: Insecta, PHYLUM: Arthropoda.   M.J.P.

DUNNOCK *Prunella modularis,* bird more properly known as the Common *accentor of Europe and the Near East, in most parts of its range restricted to coniferous forests and scrubland in upland areas, but commonly found in parks, gardens and hedgerows in Great Britain. The name dunnock is now generally preferred to the once widely used misnomer hedge-sparrow. FAMILY: Prunellidae, ORDER: Passeriformes, CLASS: Aves.

DWARF ANTELOPES, essentially small gazelles of the tribe Neotragini, the smallest living members of the Bovidae. It is uncertain whether it is a homogeneous group, or whether it is derived independently from larger gazelle-like antelopes. Only one species, the rhebok *Pelea capreolus,* is distinctive enough to be of uncertain affinity. It may be a dwarfed reedbuck rather than a dwarfed gazelle. All appear to live in pairs.

The other Dwarf antelopes are: (1) Klipspringer *Oreotragus oreotragus* is 20 in (50 cm) high and weighs 24–33 lb (11–15 kg). A rock-living antelope, with tall, truncated hoofs and thick, pithy speckled fur which protects it from sharp stones and thorns. It ranges to over 12,000 ft (3,657·6 m). It is found from South and Southwest Africa north to Ethiopia and the Red Sea Hills; in the Bongo Range, Central African Republic; and in Zaria Province, Nigeria. (2) Oribi

Dung beetles, inveterate scavengers, are related to the Sacred beetle of Ancient Egypt.

Ourebia ourebi is up to 27 in (68 cm) high and weighs 31–46 lb (14–21 kg). It has silky hair and is tawny in colour having a bare black patch under each ear like a reedbuck. It is found in tall grass and on downs, from the Cape to southern Sudan, Ethiopia, Lake Chad and Senegal. Like the klipspringer, it has a shrill whistling alarm call. It runs with its tail held high, bounding and stotting through the long grass. (3) Steinbok *Raphicerus campestris* and the grysbok *R. melanotis* and *R. sharpei* are about the same size as the klipspringer. They have coarse hair and thick smooth horns. The females are hornless. A large circular facegland is surrounded by a bare area in steinbok and grysbok and by short hairs in Sharpe's grysbok. Steinbok, from South and East Africa, have a uniform coat and no lateral hoofs; grysbok, from S.W. Cape province, have a deep rufous, speckled coat, long ears and small lateral hoofs; Sharpe's grysbok, from Natal to Tanzania is speckled tawny with no lateral hoofs. These species often hide underground, in old aardvark holes, and here the female gives birth. Grysbok scuttle away with the head straight out in front; steinbok hold the head higher and gallop. Steinbok are very aggressive while mating; the female lies down while giving birth, a rare posture among antelopes. (4) Suni *Neotragus moschatus*, Royal antelope *N. pygmaeus* and Bates's dwarf antelope *N. batesi* differ from the last mainly in their smaller size and in the horns, which point backward instead of upward. Suni are

12 in (30 cm) high, weighing 18–20 lb (8–9 kg). They are brown-grey above and white below and have ringed horns. They live in dry thicket country from Natal to Kenya, where they are very localized. Bates's dwarf antelope is a little larger with shorter horns, only $1\frac{1}{2}$ in (4 cm) long. It is brown with white underneath. Small lateral hoofs are present and it lives in lowland forest, discontinuously, in the Gabon-Cameroun district and again in the eastern Congo. The Royal antelope is the smallest of all Bovidae, only 10–$11\frac{1}{2}$ in (25–30 cm) high, with horns about $\frac{3}{4}$ in (2 cm) long. It is bright red-fawn, with a white underside. It replaces Bates's antelope in lowland forests from Sierra Leone to Ghana. In all three, the haunches are high and rounded like an agouti, the South American rodent, a typical undergrowth animal's habitus. (5) Dikdik *Madoqua swaynei, saltiana, phillipsi, guentheri* and *kirki* are very distinctive, about 12–16 in (30–40 cm) high, with a tuft of hair between the horns which point upward, and an elongated, swollen snout. The horns are ringed and the hair is long, soft and speckled. The five species are very difficult to distinguish. They occur in the Somali arid zone, south into Tanzania, and one occurs again in the Kalahari. The usual colour is a speckled grey, with an orange-red underside. When disturbed, dikdik dash off in zigzag leaps making their 'zik-zak' chirrup that gives them their name. They live in pairs in thorn thickets, browsing off juicy vegetation. The pair use defined paths through the thicket;

they defaecate in a set spot, and try to bury the dung if the ground is soft. (6) Beira *Dorcatragus megalotis* is 20–30 in (50–75 cm) high and weighs 20–24 lb (9–11 kg), more than twice as much as a dikdik. It has coarse hair, red-grey above and white below, with white eye-rings and a dark flank-stripe. The beira has big ears and long legs. It lives in rocky hills in Somalia, and is the only Dwarf antelope to live in groups; four to seven are seen together, of which one or two will be males.

Dwarf antelopes are an interesting group about which little is known. They are, nowadays, less rarely seen in captivity than formerly and appear to be small enough to have escaped much of the overhunting that has reduced their larger relatives. FAMILY: Bovidae, ORDER: Artiodactyla, CLASS: Mammalia.
C.P.G.

DWARFISM. On islands, and in other small, restricted areas, animal groups which elsewhere consist of medium or large-sized forms often show a tendency towards the evolution of dwarf varieties or species. This seems to be one way by which populations with a limited food supply can still maintain a viable population level. The Shetland pony probably originated in this way as also did the extinct pygmy elephants which lived on islands in the Malay Archipelago.

DWARF MALES, males which are very substantially smaller than the females of the same species. In most animals there is little external difference between the sexes. Only in some species with highly developed patterns of behaviour—chiefly arthropods, cephalopods and vertebrates—are males larger than the females, ornamented or more brightly coloured, or with a complex song, so that they can the better compete by fighting or display for the attention of the female. At the other extreme, sporadically throughout the animal kingdom, we find suppression of the male sex, so that the females can reproduce without ever being fertilized. This is known as parthenogenesis. A familiar example is the common Stick insect *Carausius* in which generation after generation of females lay unfertilized eggs and never a male appears.

In other species the male may not be completely suppressed. He is commonly needed to produce 'resistant' eggs. Rotifers or Wheel animalcules, for instance, reproduce in puddles for many generations without males, but as the pool begins to dry up some females produce smaller eggs, all of which hatch out into males. Females fertilized by these males then lay eggs which do not hatch immediately but are able to withstand dessication and survive in the dried mud until the next heavy rains. These male rotifers are much smaller than the females,

Dwarf males

often only a quarter as long and a hundredth of the volume of the other sex. The gut is rudimentary; they never feed and survive simply on the yolk of the egg until the time when they copulate with a female and then die soon after. They are little more than a bag of reproductive organs provided with a means of locomotion.

Amongst the insects too we find males which appear only in some generations, usually towards the autumn to fertilize eggs which will survive the winter. In aphids (such as greenfly) these males are only slightly smaller than the females, but in many of the Stick insects (except the common species which is so often kept as a pet) the males may be only half the length of the females. The lithe active males dart about seeking out the sluggish, heavy-bodied females. Even in some species in which all eggs have to be fertilized the male may be smaller than the female. Examples may be found amongst the numerous species of praying mantids in which the male may be only $\frac{1}{3}$ the length of the female. In these insects the male courts the female and begins to mate with her, but ejaculation of the sperm cannot be completed until the nervous connexions between the brain and reproductive organs have been destroyed. This is accomplished by the female chewing away at the head of the male like a stick of rock. She completes her meal once mating is finished and then goes on to produce large heavy yolky eggs.

In general we find that in species in which dwarf males occur the female produces either large eggs or live young. I know of no case of dwarf males occurring in a species where multitudinous small eggs are shed into the water or scattered about. Even among the parasitic threadworms (nematodes) where the males are almost always smaller than the females, though not excessively so, the eggs which they produce are large in comparison to the size of the body. In some species the male may be no more than $\frac{1}{6}$ the length of the female and in one species at least, *Syngamus trachealis* (a parasite of poultry, where it causes the disease known as 'gapes'), the male is permanently attached to the female and parasitic upon her; so that we have here a male parasitic upon a female of the same species which is in turn parasitic upon a bird.

A non-parasitic worm in which the male is parasitic upon the female is the vivid green *Bonellia viridis,* an animal about the size and shape of a cocktail sausage, bearing a long probosicis which forks at the tip. This proboscis can extend up to 5 ft (1·5 m) and is used to pick up animal prey, tearing small Sea squirts, for instance, off the rocks to which they are attached and passing them back to the mouth along the groove which furrows its length. In this species the male

larvae settle upon the proboscis of the female and pass into the mouth, just as if they were food. Within the pharynx, however, instead of being digested, they attach to the wall, where they complete the change to their adult shape and then creep out again through the mouth and wander over the surface of the female until they find the opening of the single nephridium—the excretory organ of these worms. The nephridium serves also as a brood pouch into which the male, no more than $\frac{1}{20}$ in (1·2 mm) long, creeps and lives out his life as a parasite of the female and fertilizes the eggs as they pass into the brood pouch.

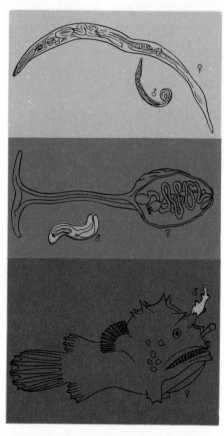

Some examples of dwarf males. Top: The common Pin worm or seatworm *Enterobius vermicularis,* a nematode parasite that often infects children, causing restlessness and insomnia. Centre: *Bonellia,* an echiuroid, in which the males are only about I mm long and live parasitically upon or within the body of a female I m long. Potentially bisexual as larvae, the independent young become females, while those attached to females develop into males. Bottom: Female Deep-sea anglerfish (see anglerfishes).

In spiders the male is appreciably smaller than the female. An extreme example is the widely distributed tropical *Nephila chrysogaster* in which the body of the female is as much as 2 in (50 mm) long. The male is no more than $\frac{1}{10}$ in (2·5 mm) long and perhaps $\frac{1}{1300}$ of the weight of the female. So ferocious are female spiders that copulation must be a rather fearsome ordeal for the tiny male who tiptoes up to his putative mate and uses

a variety of methods to court her, to distract her attention and to persuade her that he is inedible for long enough for him to inseminate her. He is then often eaten by his spouse if he cannot escape quickly enough. It has been suggested that smaller, more agile males can escape from the females more easily than larger ones and so live to fertilize a second female. If this is so then smallness and agility have a clear selective advantage and natural selection will operate towards reducing their size.

Amongst the vertebrates dwarf parasitic males occur in some of the deep-sea angler fish, but the last two examples I shall describe are drawn from the molluscs and the crustaceans respectively. Amongst the more primitive relatives of the octopus is the argonaut, which retains an external shell in the female used for brooding the young. The male is much smaller and lacks any shell. One arm of the male is modified to act as an intromittent organ and at courtship becomes detached, carrying sperm over to the female. This arm, together with the sperm it carries accounts for almost half the weight of the male and its continuing activity inside the mantle cavity of the female led early naturalists to believe that it was a parasite. After the loss of his 'hectocotylus' arm the male ceases to feed and soon dies.

Barnacles are sedentary animals and most of them live in dense stands, where copulation by means of a long extensile penis is possible between closely adjacent animals. A few barnacles, however, are solitary animals. It was here, in the genera *Ibla* and *Scalpellum,* that the existence of dwarf parasitic males was first recorded by Charles Darwin. The idea was so strange at first that he went to great lengths to satisfy himself (and his readers) that these parasites really were males of the same species as their hosts. Amongst these barnacles there is a whole range of dependency of the male upon the female. In the most extreme form the males occupy preformed cavities at the edge of the scutum (shell) of the female, in a position where they can copulate with her (though the larger host animal may be hermaphrodite, not necessarily a simple female). These small males lack mouth or gut and indeed most adult organs except those of reproduction: they are essentially larval in structure.

Dwarf males, and especially parasitic dwarf males, are found sporadically throughout the animal kingdom and are always associated with internal fertilization, and with large eggs or live young. The condition has evolved many times. In conclusion, it is perhaps worth remarking that dwarf males are often found in species where one female may be served by several males, a condition we may contrast with sealions, where one 'giant' male may serve many small females.

D.B.C.

E

EAGLES, name given to many powerful, rapacious, diurnal birds of prey (Falconiformes). Originally the name may have been applied to European members of the genera *Aquila* and *Haliaetus* (Golden eagle, Sea eagle) and later to the near relatives of these birds. All the European species except one, the Booted eagle *Hieraetus pennatus*, are large or very large rapacious birds, and perhaps appeared to merit a different name from hawks or buzzards. It was only later, when many small tropical species no larger than some buzzards, or even hawks, were discovered, that the term 'eagle' was applied to such relatively small birds of prey.

'Eagle' at present includes many widely divergent species of diurnal raptors. However, eagles divide naturally into four main groups, though not very closely related ones.

1 The Sea and Fish eagles, genera *Haliaetus* and *Ichthyophaga*, with a worldwide range with the exception of South America are typified by the European sea eagle *Haliaetus albicilla*. To these may be added the aberrant Vulturine fish eagle or Palm-nut vulture *Gypohierax angolensis* which feeds almost exclusively on the pericarp of oil palm nuts (*Elaeis guineensis*). By some authorities this group is separated as a subfamily, Haliaetinae. It seems closely related to some kites, notably the Brahminy kite *Hasliastur indus*.

2 The Snake and Serpent eagles, confined to Africa and Asia, feeding almost entirely on snakes and reptiles, typified by the European serpent or Short-toed eagle *Circaetus gallicus*. Again, these were sometimes separated as a subfamily, Circaetinae, and are rather distinct. Their nearest apparent relatives are harriers *Circus* spp.

3 The Harpy and Crested eagles and their relatives, a rather loose ill-defined group, mainly South American, but with representatives in the Philippines and New Guinea. Typified by the Harpy eagle *Harpya harpyja*, these are large or very large raptors, allied to buzzards (*Buteo* and related genera) and sometimes joined with them in a subfamily, Buteoninae. They are, in fact, little more than extra-large and sometimes unusually rapacious buzzards.

4 The true 'Booted' or Aquiline eagles, which differ from all the others in that the tarsus is feathered to the toes. They are worldwide, but more common in the Old World, typified by the Golden eagle *Aquila chrysaetos*, with many small forest species included in the genus *Spizaetus*. These were sometimes placed in a subfamily Aquilinae.

These four groups, sometimes classed for convenience in subfamilies, are, in the most modern classification of the Falconiformes, included in one large family Accipitridae. There are so many intermediate types that subfamilies are not truly tenable. They vary in size from the largest and most formidable of all birds of prey (and accordingly, the most formidable of all living birds) the Harpy eagle and Philippine monkey-eating eagle *Pithecophaga jefferyi* to relatively tiny species such as the Nias Island serpent eagle *Spilornis cheela asturinus* and Ayres hawk-eagle *Hieraetus dubius*. These species are smaller than most buzzards and in function overlap with smaller hawks.

The Sea and Fish eagles, of the genera *Haliaetus* (eight species) and *Ichthyophaga* (two species), occur in all continents except South America and on many East Indian islands. One species occurs in Madagascar, but they are absent from oceanic islands. They are most varied in Europe and continental Asia (four *Haliaetus* species and two *Ichthyophaga*), with one species of *Haliaetus* each in North America (see Bald eagle), Africa south of the Sahara, Mada-

Winged terror of the Philippines forests, the Monkey-eating eagle *Pithecophaga jefferyi*.

gascar, India, Malaysia and Australasia, and the Solomon Islands. They include two huge species, the European sea eagle or erne *Haliaetus albicilla* and Steller's sea eagle *Haliaetus pelagicus*. The latter is perhaps the grandest and most impressive of all diurnal raptors—a huge bird, weighing 15 lb (6½ kg) or more, with a wing-span approaching 8 ft (2½ m), and capable of killing animals as large as a seal calf. No Sea eagle or Fish eagle is very small, the smallest of the genus *Haliaetus* being the Madagascar fish eagle *Haliaetus vociferoides*. The two species in the genus *Ichthyophaga*, confined to the larger rivers, lakes and shorelines of tropical Asia (including some islands) are smaller.

The Vulturine fish eagle, occurring in those parts of tropical Africa where the oil palm grows, is a very strange vegetarian raptor, probably related to this group of eagles on the one side, and forming a link with the Old World vultures on the other. In the end, however, it may prove not to be related to either.

Sea, Fish and Vulturine fish eagles share a number of features. They have bare tarsi and adults show much white, especially on the head and tail; immature birds are brown. They are all more or less confined to aquatic habitats, large lakes, rivers or the seashore. Some, for example, the African fish eagle *Haliaetus vocifer*, are numerous and familiar in such habitats. Pallas' sea eagle, chiefly of interior Asia (and hence wrongly called a Sea eagle) is perhaps the least aquatic of the Eurasian species, while the aberrant, frugivorous Vulturine fish eagle occurs scattered through savannahs lacking large bodies of water; it is nevertheless aquatic in, for instance, mangrove swamps. All these eagles except the Vulturine fish eagle, have spicules on the feet adapted to grasping fishes, but not to such an extreme degree as the osprey *Pandion*. Fish is important in the diet of all, even the Vulturine fish eagle. Two species, the Bald eagle *H. leucocephalus* and Steller's sea eagle, feed much on stranded and dying Pacific salmon. Besides fish, they eat carrion and some water birds, but seldom do they eat mammals, except for the young of aquatic species such as seals.

The Snake and Serpent eagles include five genera, four of which (*Circaetus, Terathopius, Dryotriorchis* and *Eutriorchis*) are African, and one Eurasian representative, the Short-toed or Serpent eagle, *Circaetus gallicus*. Asian Snake eagles mainly belong to the genus *Spilornis*. The Crested serpent eagle *S. cheela* is widespread and occurs in tropical continental Asia and on many islands. The five other species are all insular, in Malaysia and Indonesia, and some of them (e.g. *Spilornis klossi*, of the Nicobars) are very small.

Most Snake Eagles have bare tarsi and short, powerful toes, well adapted to grasping and quickly immobilizing quick-moving and possibly venomous serpents. They are not immune to snake venom, and to kill snakes they depend upon agility and, perhaps, dense feathers and heavily scaled legs. All have rather large, often crested heads, with very large yellow eyes. They vary from the large European snake eagle, the Brown snake eagle *Circaetus cinereus* and continental forms of the Crested serpent eagle, all larger than large buzzards, to the smallest of all eagles, the diminutive Nias Island serpent eagle and the Nicobar serpent eagle, each smaller than many large sparrowhawks. All feed, mainly or for preference, on reptiles, especially snakes or frogs, and rarely take mammals or birds.

The most unusual of the Snake eagle

Bald eagle *Haliaetus leucocephalus*, the North American eagle whose existence is threatened.

group is the African bateleur *Terathopius ecaudatus*, one of the most specialized and remarkable of all eagles. Adults have exceptionally long wings and a very short tail. In immature birds the tail is longer. The bateleur's relationship to other Snake eagles is shown by similar development of the young, which is mainly brown, unlike the spectacular black, chestnut and white adult. Bateleurs appear to be specialized for high-speed gliding, and spend most of the day traversing the African skies, usually at 2–500 ft (60–150 m), at an air-speed of about 35–55 mph (56–88 kph). They hold their exceptionally long wings with a pronounced upward slant (dihedral) and, having little tail, apparently steer by canting from side to side—hence the name 'bateleur' (derived from the French name for old-time tightrope walkers, who carried a long pole to aid balance). Bateleurs eat many snakes, but also take some mammals and ground birds and will eat carrion. They are also piratical, chasing and robbing vultures, a habit possibly derived from carrion-feeding.

Less specialized are the Congo serpent eagle *Dryotriorchis spectabilis* and the Madagascar serpent eagle *Eutriorchis astur*. The former lives in the deep gloom of the densest tropical African forests, and has unusually large eyes, even for a Snake eagle, which is an adaptation to its habitat. The Madagascar serpent eagle is a link between the African snake eagles, *Circaetus,* and the Asian *Spilornis*. Very little is known about either, even their nests have not been found; and, owing to destruction of habitat, the Madagascar snake eagle's status is now uncertain.

The buteonine, or Harpy-like eagles include six large species, two in the genera *Harpyhaliaetus,* and one in *Morphnus, Harpia, Harpyopsis* and *Pithecophaga*. The first three occur only in South American forests, *Harpyopsis* in New Guinea and *Pithecophaga* in the Philippines. They are little known, and though they may be quite common the nests of several have not been found. Although apparently related to buzzards, this group includes both the largest and most powerful eagle, the Harpy eagle, and probably the rarest of the world's eagles, the Philippine monkey-eating eagle.

The Harpy eagle is huge, females weighing about 15 lb (6½ kg) or more, males 8–10 lb (3½–4½ kg). It ranges widely in tropical South and Central American forests. Harpies are rather unlike buzzards in that they are apparently fierce and powerful predators, feeding upon large forest mammals such as monkeys, agoutis and sloths. It is probable that a female Harpy eagle is about as large and heavy as an eagle can be while still being able to fly dexterously enough among trees to be an effective predator. However, so little is known about the field habits of these great birds that it is unwise to be dogmatic. A female Harpy has legs almost as thick as a child's wrist and massive feet with huge curving talons. A falconer who kept one observed that the problem was not to get her to come to his fist, but to be well enough padded to withstand the impact of her arrival. In addition, the Harpy has a flaring double crest which makes it look truly savage.

Nearly as large as the Harpy, the Philippine monkey-eating eagle is confined to the larger Philippine Islands and probably only survives on Samar and Mindanao. Perhaps 50 pairs now exist, since this species is threatened by increasing destruction of habitat through human overpopulation, by the traffic in wild birds for zoos and by the prestige value of an eagle trophy. Efforts are now being made to conserve the remaining population.

The other eagles in this group are smaller and less powerful, but still large predators. They appear to behave like large forest buzzards. However, knowledge is sketchy; none

The Golden eagle (above), up to 2 m across the spread wings, inhabits mountainous areas of the northern hemisphere. (Below) Pallas's fishing eagle *Haliaetus leucoryphus*, of central Asia.

The African fish eagle (above left) has been given the specific name *vocifer*, and the common name of Voice of Africa, for its persistent calling. (Above right) The White-bellied sea eagle *Haliaetus leucogaster*, of Celebes and the Australian region. (Right, below) The White-tailed sea eagle or European sea eagle.

has been properly observed, either at the nest or elsewhere.

The true, or Booted eagles, with feathered tarsi, include 30 species in nine genera: ten in *Spizaetus,* nine in *Aquila,* five in *Hieraetus,* and one in *Spizastur, Lophaetus, Ictinaetus, Stephanoaetus, Croaetus* and *Polemaetus.* The larger species include all the best known eagles in the world, e.g. the holarctic Golden eagle, the African Verreaux's eagle *Aquila verreauxi* and the Crowned eagle *Stephano-aetus coronatus.* The smaller species are less well known, but even some of these are very much better known than most eagles, e.g. the African Ayres hawk-eagle *Hieraetus dubius.* The least known are some small forest *Spizaetus* species of Asia or South America. The African Crowned eagle is perhaps the most intimately known of all the world's eagles, one nest-site having been watched for 20 years, another for ten.

These eagles vary from very small species such as Ayres' hawk-eagle, or Wallace's hawk-eagle *Spizaetus nanus* of Malaysia to very large and powerful eagles such as the African Crowned and Martial eagle *Polemaetus bellicosus* and Siberian Golden eagle, sufficiently large and powerful to kill wolves. Wild individuals feed upon large mammals (e.g. Crowned eagles), game-birds (Martial and Golden eagles), smaller mammals (Tawny and Spotted eagles *Aquila rapax, A. clanga* and *A. pomavina*), frogs (Spotted eagles) and birds (Ayres' hawk-eagle). They range the world's habitats from the Arctic to

the Equator, but no further south than temperate Tasmania. South American *Spizaetus* species live in tropical forest. Half the species live in open country and half in forests or heavy woodland, with some intermediates. In Africa the Martial eagle inhabits savannahs, while the Crowned eagle lives in forests. Forest species are short-winged and long-tailed, resembling goshawks in silhouette. These booted species are the most widespread and successful of all eagles.

There is some doubt as to whether the Indian Black eagle *Ictinaetus malayensis* is an eagle or some form of aberrant kite. Superficially, the young resemble kites, but the general habits of the species resemble eagles. The feet are peculiar, with long thin, not strongly curved, claws unlike the powerful clutching talons of most eagles. Black eagles use these specialized feet to snatch whole nests of birds, subsequently eating the contents. The primaries are very long and soft, possibly an adaptation to slow flight. The affinities of this unusual species are not yet clear.

The typical eagles, genus *Aquila,* are large or very large, varying from the rather small Wahlberg's eagle *A. wahlbergi* to huge Golden, Verreaux's and Wedge-tailed eagles, spanning 7–8 ft (2–2½ m) in large females, and able to kill mammals as large as a deer calf. The Tawny eagle *Aquila rapax,* widespread in open country in Asia and Africa, is probably the most common of the world's large eagles. It feeds on small mammals and carrion, and is strongly piratical, pursuing other species to obtain prey. All *Aquila* species are brown, immature birds and adults alike, except for Verreaux's eagle, which is a magnificent coal-black species with a white patch on the back. It feeds almost exclusively on Rock hyrax (*Procavia* and *Heterohyrax*), the conies of the Bible.

Hawk-eagles, of the genera *Hieraetus* and *Spizastur*, link the open country *Aquila* species and the forest *Lophaetus, Spizaetus, Stephanoaetus* and *Oroaetus*. Bonelli's eagle *Hieraetus fasciatus* is considerably bigger than the others and, for its size, perhaps the most potent predator of all. In Africa the resident race the African hawk-eagle *H. f. spilogaster* kills much the same range of prey as the much larger Martial eagle; the others are smaller. Three, the Booted eagle *H. pennatus,* the Ayres' eagle and the Chestnut-bellied hawk-eagle *H. kieneri,* specialize in swift pursuit of woodland and forest birds, resembling goshawks more than eagles. The Australian little eagle *H. morphnoides,* feeds on small mammals in mixed open country. Scarcely anything is known of the South American *Spizastur melanoleucus.*

Most species of the genus *Spizaetus* are also little known; the nests of five species have not been found. However, the large and powerful Mountain hawk-eagle *S. nipalensis* and the Changeable hawk-eagle *S. cirrhatus* are quite well known. The latter has several races and colour phases, some crested. The melanistic crested types resemble the African long-crested eagle *Lophaetus occipitalis,* which is black, with a long crest. The Mountain hawk-eagle is the Asian counterpart of the African crowned eagle and the South American Isidor's eagle *Oreaetus isidori.* All are powerful birds capable of killing quite large mammals. Crowned eagles can kill mammals up to 35 lb (15½ kg) in weight; and at the nest they are extremely dangerous.

The Martial eagle is the largest, but not the most powerful of all 'booted' eagles. A female may weigh 14 lb (6·3 kg), and span almost 8 ft (2½ m), as large as, or larger than the largest Siberian golden eagles. Martial eagles are rather shy, living on open plains or savannah and feeding mainly on gamebirds. They seldom kill large mammals and are not dangerous.

It will now be clear how varied are the predatory functions of eagles, from killing small forest birds to large mammals, frogs, snakes and fishes. The majority are undoubtedly beneficial to man, but a certain number are said by shepherds or game preservers to do harm. All these are large or spectacular species. They include the European sea eagle, Golden eagle, Wedge-tailed eagle *Aquila audax,* Verreaux's eagle and Martial eagle. The Golden eagle in America and the Wedge-tailed eagle of

Australia have been destroyed in very large numbers in systematic campaigns. In Britain the European sea eagle was exterminated early in this century, mainly because of alleged damage to sheep and finally by collectors. These campaigns of extermination have never been based on objective observations of the feeding of these birds and their true effect on the population of lambs, or other possible prey. On the contrary, they have been wholly based on ignorant and blind prejudice.

A Golden eagle needs about 9 oz (250 gm) of flesh per day, about 7% of the eagle's body-weight. A pair and their offspring require about 550 lb (250 kg) of flesh a year, but must kill about 15% more, or about 660 lb (300 kg) altogether, to keep alive. Much of the winter and spring food is carrion, as then there are abundant dead deer and sheep. A pair might possibly kill two or three lambs per year at most, less than 1% of those available in an average territory of 11,000 acres (4,450 ha). Any adverse effect is negligible, and easily balanced by the benefit to sheep-farmers of hares, foxes and other animals and birds essentially injurious to sheep which the birds destroy. In South Africa Verreaux's eagle can find so many hyrax in a territory that it has no need to kill sheep. If the entire American population of Golden eagles ate nothing but lambs in the southwest during the winter, they could not cause an appreciable loss in the lamb crop. In Australia the main food of the Wedge-tailed eagle is rabbits, the country's worst pest and any lambs taken may well be dead before they are picked up. Eagles are not proven to be seriously harmful to man anywhere in the world. The majority are neutral, or beneficial to man's interests, and can be ignored, or should be actively protected.

The largest animals killed by any eagles are young deer, young seals (Steller's and European sea eagles) or young antelope (Crowned eagle). The Harpy eagle, immensely powerful, can probably kill larger mammals than any, but its full range of prey is unknown. A Crowned eagle, itself weighing 9 lb (4 kg) has been known to kill a bushbuck of 35 lb (15½ kg) about four times its own weight. Very large kills are dismembered skilfully, and the portions hidden in trees until needed. Most eagles kill prey of half their own weight, or less. Some, such as Tawny and Long-crested eagles, live like buzzards on abundant small animals.

Despite their varied origin and relationships, there are many similarities between the known life-histories of most species of eagles. They are rather long-lived, as are many other large birds. Several large species have lived 40 to 50 years in captivity, for example Golden and Imperial eagles, but the oldest acceptable record is for a bateleur, still alive at 55. In the wild state eagles have much

shorter lives. The average life span must be related to the breeding replacement rate, which on average is less than one young per pair per annum, but varies from 0·4 to 0·8, and occasionally more. Probably about three young in four die before sexual maturity, so a pair would take, on average, four to eight years to replace themselves. Probably the wild life-spans are of this order.

Eagles apparently mate for life but if one of the individuals of a pair dies, the other obtains a new mate as soon as possible. This seems to be not very difficult, even in rather rare species; unmated eagles can probably find each other even when very widely scattered. The pair-bond is usually maintained even outside the breeding season and eagles will often roost together, although they may have been apart all day. Whether this applies to migrant as well as to sedentary species is unknown, but it seems likely, for some migrant species display to one another in winter. When a mate is missing, the survivor probably obtains another from a small un-

Eagle is an ill-defined term for large birds of prey and it is sometimes used for others such as this kite *Haliastur sphenurus* which is called the Whistling eagle.

mated adult population. Adults sometimes mate with immature birds, at least temporarily, even in abundant species. Immature birds cannot breed until they achieve adult plumage, which is usually from three to four years after hatching.

A pair of eagles lives in a loosely held territory, or home range. Few species are so aggressive at or near the nest as buzzards or the larger falcons. They seem, rather, not to mind near neighbours, or perhaps to maintain their territories by subtle methods. African Fish eagles tolerate others of their kind flying over their nests, and two pairs have nested successfully within 600 ft (180 m) of each other. On the other hand, Martial eagles and Golden eagles maintain very large home ranges without any obvious sign of boundary conflicts. It is possible that eagles can observe aggressive behaviour that would be almost invisible to human beings.

Somewhere within the home range eagles have one or more nests. In most species these are used repeatedly, being added to and repaired until they become very large. Snake eagles are a complete exception to this rule. Most Snake eagles make small flimsy nests every year or two. These may be close to, or far from, the previous years' nests and are always much more difficult to find than other eagles' nests. Other eagles may have from one to ten more permanent nests per pair. Tropical species usually have fewer nests than those of cold wet climates. In Scotland Golden eagles, constantly disturbed by human beings, may build more nests in an effort to obtain seclusion. Eagles' nests are among the largest of all birds' nests. They are built of sticks on cliffs, in trees, or rarely on the ground and some may become towering structures 15 ft (4½ m) high and 4–5 ft (1–1½ m) across at the top. Most are smaller, and the largest known nests are in temperate climates. Some of these are in sites used for centuries by a succession of different eagles and a change of mates does not necessarily mean that a new nest will be constructed. Smaller eagles naturally build smaller nests, but they may be equally faithful to the site. However in some, such as the African Tawny and Long-crested eagles, the site is changed more often and is seldom occupied for more than five years.

Occupation of the site is always preceded by nest repair, usually by adding green branches or sprigs to the existing nest; even Snake eagles do this. This is not adornment, but acts as a lining, and is also associated with sexual ceremonies such as nest relief, or feeding. A nest with fresh green branches will not necessarily contain eggs later, but eggs are seldom laid without some fresh material being added to the nest.

All eagles lay small clutches, one or two, the most prolific being the kite-like Sea and Fish eagles, which often lay three eggs.

Bateleur, from the French for 'circus performer', this African eagle performs somersaults in the air.

Many, including most Snake eagles, lay only one. Eggs are usually incubated by the female, less often by the male but when two are laid, the male is more likely to incubate. Incubation periods are long, from 43–49 days. This even applies to some small eagles such as Wahlberg's or Ayres', smaller than buzzards, that have much shorter incubation periods. The incubation periods of many species are not known, or are inaccurately recorded.

The eggs are laid, and hatch, at intervals of several days. In many species, notably of the true or Booted eagles, the eldest hatched young is much larger than those hatched later, which it invariably kills. The parents do nothing whatever to interfere in this 'Cain and Abel battle', which may not be connected with shortage of food, but is automatic when two young eagles are placed in the nest together. They always fight, and the stronger nearly always wins. This sort of struggle is not so fierce, or fatal, in the kite-like Sea and Fish eagles, which more often rear two or three young.

The development of the young resembles that of other birds of prey. The nestling is at first downy and helpless, requiring constant care. A second and thicker coat of down grows after two to three weeks, and brooding is reduced. Feathers begin to come through the down from $\frac{2}{3}-\frac{2}{5}$ of the way through the

fledgling period and cover the body when the eaglet is rather more than half-grown. The bill and the feet, used for feeding, develop faster at first. In Snake eagles and the bateleur, which nest in very open sites, the upper side of the body becomes feathered before the lower side. Feathering, and the development of bill and feet, means that the female adult is released to take part in killing prey as she can then leave the young alone in the nest. In the last third of the fledging period the young is visited only with food, sometimes not even every day.

The male often feeds the female while she is incubating, but some females leave the nest to feed. After hatching the role of the sexes is usually clear-cut. The male does most, or all of the killing until the young is partly feathered; at this stage he is killing for himself, the female and the brood. Once the young is feathered, the female can assist in providing the food, thus halving the male's duties. Apparently this has little effect on brood survival; most eaglets that have survived their first two weeks grow to leave the nest.

Eaglets fly of their own accord between 60–125 days after hatching. In a tree they may first jump to other branches, and on a cliff, they will make a short flight to another ledge. For several weeks after its first flight the eaglet flies weakly, for the stiff, but still rowing wing and tail quills have yet to harden. In some species, for instance, young Golden eagles bred in the north, the young must migrate to warmer climates within a month or two of the first flight. An eaglet may still depend on its parents for food for some time longer; in the Harpy and African crowned eagles, the period of dependence is very long. In the Crowned eagle the young is fed by the parents for 9–11 months after its first flight, and the pair cannot normally breed more than once every two years. On average, they rear four out of five young hatched. Contrary to general belief, the parents do not drive the young away; rather it becomes independent of its own accord and releases the parents from their duties.

The potential number, one to three, of young reared by any pair of eagles is reduced by infertile eggs, nestling losses (especially through a 'Cain and Abel battle'), sometimes by starvation or predation, and also accident. The actual number of young reared is usually half, or less, of the potential, but in Crowned eagles, with their very long period of dependence, it is about 80% of the potential. Probably not more than one young eagle in four becomes sexually mature, so that adults must be moderately long-lived for any species to survive at all. FAMILY: Accipitridae, ORDER: Falconiformes, CLASS: Aves. L.H.B.

EAGLE, KING OF THE BIRDS. The role of eagles in mythology is vast. One of the most familiar and widespread stories, known to North American Indians as well as in Europe, is that concerning the competition to decide who should be the King of the Birds; the crown is to go to the bird who can fly the highest. The eagle, who is the obvious candidate, appears to win but the wren hides among the eagle's feathers and flutters a short but decisive distance above the eagle when the latter has reached its ceiling. According to some versions, the eagle attacked the wren, damaging its tail feathers, which is why a wren now always flies near the ground. A common theme in other eagle legends is of the enmity between eagles and wrens.

EAGLE RAYS, a family of ray-like cartilaginous fishes with a whip-like tail usually with a venomous spine at its base. The expanded pectoral fins are used to propel the fish through the water with considerable grace, the tail being held stiffly behind. The Eagle ray *Myliobatis aquila* of the Mediterranean and eastern Atlantic can be distinguished from similar Sting rays of these coasts by its prominent head, which is raised well above the level of the pectoral wings. The back is smooth and brown, the undersides a rather dirty white and the tail black.

It grows to about 4 ft (1·2 m) in length and feeds chiefly on molluscs which are crushed with the powerful pavement of teeth in the jaws.

As in all members of this family, the young are born alive, having hatched previously within the uterus of the female. At least in the American Pacific coast species, *M. californicus,* the young are born tail first, the poison spine being soft and sheathed in tissue until after birth. In certain areas, such as San Francisco Bay, Eagle rays are a considerable pest of commercial clam and oyster beds, which must be protected with fences of stakes.

Members of the genus *Rhinoptera* are sometimes placed in a separate family, the Rhinopteridae or Cow-nosed rays. They resemble the Eagle rays in having a curious fleshy fold or lobe below the eyes but it is better developed and is split in the middle to give left and right portions looking like the horns of a cow. These fishes can measure up to 7 ft (2·1 m) from tip to tip of the pectoral 'wings'.

The Duck-billed rays (*Aetobatus, Aetomylaeus*) differ from the two previous groups in having only a single but broad band of molar-like teeth in the jaws (there being seven to nine bands in the other species). FAMILY: Myliobatidae, ORDER: Hypotremata, CLASS: Chondrichthyes.

EAR, the receptor organ for sound. It usually has an outer membrane, the tympanum, which can be set vibrating by sound waves and which stimulates sensory cells directly or indirectly by its motion. An outer ear is present in some animals, and it is this

that is referred to as the 'ear' in common speech, although it is more correctly termed the pinna or conch. It consists of a tuft of feathers in birds, and a tuft of hairs or a flap of body tissue in mammals. The pinna helps to collect sound waves and aids in the localization of sound sources.

There are many different kinds of hearing organs occurring within the animal kingdom and it is sometimes difficult to decide which should be called ears. Some hairs on the bodies of insects respond to airborne sounds of low frequency, but are also highly sensitive to touch and air movements. An ear, however, is usually thought of as a compact organ, specifically sensitive to sound. The lyriform organs of spiders, situated near the tips of the legs, and the subgenual organs of insects, situated just below the knee, are both extremely sensitive to vibrations of the substrate. They could be regarded as ears, but in insects the term is usually reserved for organs which have a tympanum. Crickets and long-horned grasshoppers have a tympanal organ near to the subgenual organ on the forelegs, which is very sensitive to sound. Similar organs are found at the base of the abdomen in grasshoppers, cicadas and some moths.

In amphibians, birds and reptiles, the tympanum lies on the surface of the head, but in mammals it is sunk at the end of a canal leading into the skull. In the course of evolution, small bones once involved in the jaw articulation have come to form part of the middle ear, and transmit the vibrations of the tympanum to fluid-filled cavities in the bone which constitute the inner ear. Amphibia, reptiles and birds have a single bone in the

Photograph of section through rear part of the head of a Guinea pig showing the cochlea on each side.

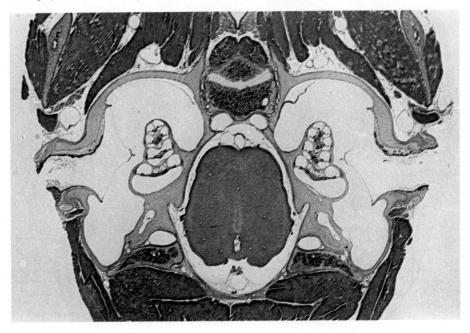

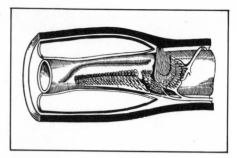

Diagram of the ear in an insect, showing a longitudinal section with the subgenual organ on the foreleg of a long-horned grasshopper, which is very sensitive to sound.

middle ear, the *columella auris,* but mammals have three: the *malleus* (hammer), *incus* (anvil) and *stapes* (footplate).

The inner ear consists basically of three fluid-filled interconnected cavities: the utricle, saccule and lagena. The semi-circular canals arise from the utricle and respond to movements of the head, while receptors in all three cavities respond to the position of the head. In fishes, in which an outer and middle ear is lacking, receptor cells in the lagena and the saccule respond to sound. Ostariophysid fishes (which include the carps and catfishes) have a row of bones connecting the gas-filled swimbladder, which acts as a sound collector, to the inner ear. The lagena of crocodiles, birds and mammals has become lengthened to form a cochlea, which is essentially a tube divided throughout most of its length by the basilar membrane which is lined with sensory cells. In mammals, the cochlea is very long and coiled into a spiral, and the receptor cells for hearing which line the basilar membrane are known collectively as the organ of Corti. The middle ear bones transmit vibrations to the fluid of the cochlea which cause the basilar membrane to oscillate, so stimulating the organ of Corti. See hearing. P.E.H.

EARS AS SIGNALS. Although the function of external ears or pinnae is to collect sound waves and channel them into the middle ear, the pinnae of some mammals have developed a secondary use as signals that transmit information to members of the same species. Thus, a frightened dog lays its ears back against its head. The ears are also laid back in a cat that is on the defensive. A horse, on the other hand, lays its ears back when threatening but pricks and turns them forwards when friendly.

EARED SEALS, members of the family Otariidae, one of the two families of the order *Pinnipedia, the other being the *Phocidae or Earless seals. There are two sub families: the Otariinae containing all the *sea lions, and the Arctocephalinae containing

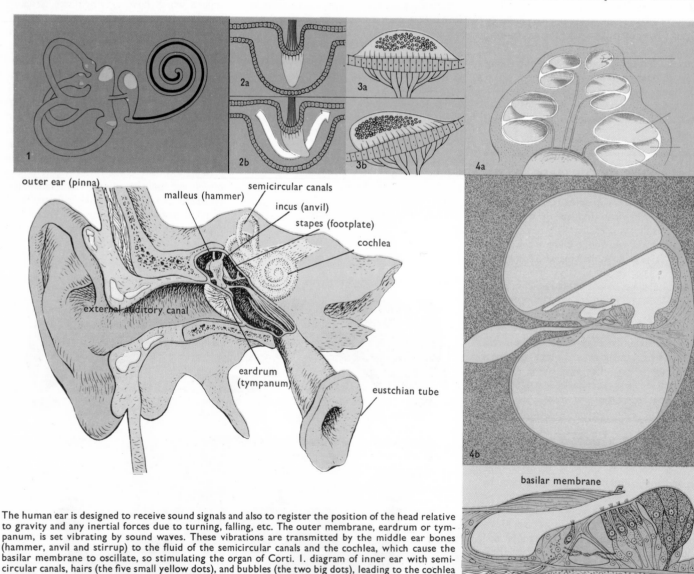

outer ear (pinna)
malleus (hammer)
semicircular canals
incus (anvil)
stapes (footplate)
cochlea
external auditory canal
eardrum (tympanum)
eustchian tube
basilar membrane

The human ear is designed to receive sound signals and also to register the position of the head relative to gravity and any inertial forces due to turning, falling, etc. The outer membrane, eardrum or tympanum, is set vibrating by sound waves. These vibrations are transmitted by the middle ear bones (hammer, anvil and stirrup) to the fluid of the semicircular canals and the cochlea, which cause the basilar membrane to oscillate, so stimulating the organ of Corti. 1. diagram of inner ear with semicircular canals, hairs (the five small yellow dots), and bubbles (the two big dots), leading to the cochlea (black); 2. a and b show the functioning of the hairs which register vibrations; 3. a and b show the functioning of the bubbles which register the position of the head relative to gravity; 4. a, b and c portray the actual hearing, c. being the organ of Corti, a. part of the cochlea, b. cross section through the cochlea.

the Fur seals. All these otariids have short external ears, furled and about 1 in (2·5 cm) long, and are able to bring their hindflippers forwards underneath their bodies. Thus on land they can make some attempt at four-footed walking, and that they are reasonably efficient at this is demonstrated by the antics of sealions in circuses. In water they are truly graceful, their very large foreflippers being used almost to fly through the water with an oar-like movement, while the hind-flippers are stretched out behind, soles together, like a rudder. The foreflippers are large, the first digit longer and stronger than the others. The spaces between the digits are padded out with fibrous tissue and the whole covered in black skin. The nails are small nodules. The digits of the hindflippers extend beyond the normal flipper outline, and are elongated by cartilaginous extensions. The three middle digits bear claws which can be used for scratching when the flipper exten-sions are folded back. On land the hind-flippers are frequently fanned backwards and forwards, causing cold air to pass over the naked flipper with its excellent blood supply, thus cooling the animal. When at sea otariids may often be seen with bodies submerged and just the flippers waving above the sur-face of the sea.

The sealions have harsh coats composed mainly of guard hairs, and the adult males often have a thick mane on the shoulders. Fur seals have, underneath the guard hairs, a thick coat of fine fur hairs and it is these that make the seal coats of commerce.

There is more disparity in size between male and female otariids than occurs in true seals (except for the Elephant seal). Adult male otariids are about 2–3 ft (0·6–0·9 m) longer than the females and considerably heavier; a bull Northern sealion *Eumetopias* of 10 ft (3 m) long may weigh 2240 lb (1016 kg), while a female of 7 ft 6 in (2·3 m) will weigh about 600 lb (272 kg).

The northern hemisphere contains two genera of sealions and two of Fur seals. The Northern sealion lives along the shores of the North Pacific from Japan through the Aleutian Islands to the Santa Barbara Islands, USA, and the Californian sealion *Zalophus* from San Francisco probably to Cedros Island, Lower California. The two Fur seals are the Northern Fur seal *Callor-inus* from the Pribilof Islands and the Guada-lupe fur seal *Arctocephalus philippii*. The southern hemisphere contains the Southern sealion *Otaria*, found from about Rio de Janeiro to the Falkland Islands and up to Peru, the Australian sealion *Neophoca* from the southerly shores of Western and South Australia, and Hooker's sealion *Phocarctos* from the Auckland and Campbell Islands, south of New Zealand. Also in the south occur the various species of the Southern fur seal *Arctocephalus* which live on some of the

shores of the southern continents and on many of the circumpolar oceanic islands. FAMILY: Otariidae, ORDER: Pinnipedia, CLASS: Mammalia. J.E.K.

EARLESS MONITOR *Lanthanotus bor-neensis,* or Earless lizard, the only genus and species of the family Lanthanotidae. It is a most unimpressive lizard 1½ ft (46 cm) long, with a dorso-ventrally flattened body, short limbs and tiny eyes. After its discovery in Sarawak in 1878 by the Austrian zoologist Franz Steindachner it was hardly ever found again and only a very few museums own a specimen. Even expeditions that set out especially to find this rare lizard had little success. It was only in the years after 1960 that the researchers Tom and Barbara Harrisson came across it by accident. With the aid of the local people they found many more after this in the wet soil, fields and forests of Sarawak and even in the irrigation ditches of the rice fields. *Lanthanotus borneensis* is excellently camouflaged: the elongated body is earthy brown, the small scales on head and body are interrupted by 6 to 10 longitudinal rows of larger cone-shaped scales that extend to the tail. The legs are very short, the movable lower lid of the tiny eyes has a transparent scale or window. The Earless monitor moves in a twisting manner, the short legs helping by pushing. Earless monitors avoid bright lights; apparently they are only active during the night and in their subterranean tunnels. They will lie motionless in their hide-outs or in shallow water for hours and days with only the nose protruding from time to time to breathe. If disturbed they flatten their already flat bodies even further and if taken in the hand they try to bite with their long pointed teeth. Nothing is known about their feeding or breeding habits in the wild; but some were kept alive in captivity for several years on small pieces of sole.

The Earless monitor has a special interest because it seems to be closely related to snakes. It is not a direct ancestor of snakes but gives a good impression of what the snake ancestor could have looked like as a subter-ranean reptile with degenerate limbs and eyes. The species is confined to Sarawak, Borneo, which suggests it is a relict species. FAMILY: Lanthanotidae, ORDER: Squamata, CLASS: Reptilia. K.K.

EARTHWORMS, so called because they burrow in the soil, are widely distributed and often occur in large numbers, for they feed mainly on decaying organic matter within the soil itself, which is usually relatively plentiful.

One of the hazards of a terrestrial way of life is the risk of desiccation. Earthworms overcome this largely by burrowing in soil. The cuticle surrounding the worm is very thin

Earthworms pairing.

and permeable unlike that of, for example, an insect. Consequently, it provides very little check on water loss, although it affords an efficient means of entry of oxygen for respiratory purposes and release of carbon dioxide. Earthworms have some behavioural adaptations, however, which serve to minimize water loss. Usually they confine themselves to damp soil and only come out of their burrows at night, when the drying influence of the sun is past and when the relative humidity is higher than during the day. This behaviour also aids the earthworm in avoiding predators such as birds, a particular advantage since an earthworm is relatively defenceless. They rarely emerge completely from their burrows. In hot or dry weather they move deeper into the soil, thereby tending to keep in moist conditions. Nevertheless, earthworms have evolved the ability to withstand losing a very large proportion of their body water, which helps them to survive arid conditions for longer than would otherwise be the case. They keep the surface of the body moist by secreting a viscous mucus from innumerable glands in the skin.

Several other adaptations to the subterranean way of life can be seen. The head region bears no appendages such as the cirri and palps of a ragworm, which might hinder the passage of the worm through the soil, or become damaged by it. Animals inhabiting dark places generally have poorly developed eyes, or none at all. An earthworm is no exception, for there are no large eyes such as are frequently found among other annelids, like the ragworm. There are, however, microscopic sense organs sensitive to light, distributed mainly near the ends of the worm, the areas most likely to receive light. There are also minute receptors sensitive to chemicals, touch and vibrations. There are probably taste receptors in the mouth, for an earthworm seems capable of some discrimination and choice over the leaves it pulls into the burrow for food.

The earthworm feeds either on such leaves pulled into the burrow with the aid of its suctorial pharynx, or by digesting the organic matter present among the particles of soil which it swallows when burrowing in earth otherwise too firm to penetrate. A muscular gizzard near the anterior end of the gut serves to break up compacted soil particles into smaller ones, with the result that digestion and absorption of the organic material within the intestine is more efficient. The uncoiled intestine has a large infolding along its length, which serves to increase its internal surface area, thereby increasing the quantity of digestive enzymes released and the efficiency of absorption of digested material. Undigested matter is extruded from the anus on to the surface of the soil as the familiar worm casts.

These casts give some indication of the

valuable effects earthworms have upon the soil. The burrows aerate and loosen the earth. The grinding action of the gizzard results in the material of the casts being finely powdered, thus serving to break up the soil. The casts also contain some partially digested organic matter and digested material which has not been absorbed, so that organic matter in the soil tends to be broken down by earthworm action. As the casts are deposited on the surface, earthworms also serve to 'turn over' the soil.

An earthworm moves by waves of muscular contraction and relaxation which pass along the length of the body, so that a particular region is alternately thin and extended or shortened and thickened. A good grip on the walls of the burrow is aided by the spiny outgrowths of the body wall called chaetae. (See Oligochaetes for some account of an earthworm's method of movement and

of the chaetae.) The nervous system consists of ganglia in the head and other ganglia at intervals on a long nerve cord, lying below the gut, which gives off a series of paired nerves one of the functions of which is to co-ordinate movement. The ganglia co-ordinate the responses of the worm in the light of the information gathered by its receptors, but they are relatively unspecialized, and can be removed from an earthworm without causing any very marked effects. Running along the nerve cord are several specialized nerve fibres called giant fibres, which are responsible for the ability of an earthworm to retract itself very rapidly into its burrow when disturbed.

Oxygen for respiration is absorbed through the thin, moist cuticle, and passes readily into the blood, for the skin is well supplied with blood vessels. The oxygen is transported to all the tissues by the blood system, in combination with the specialized

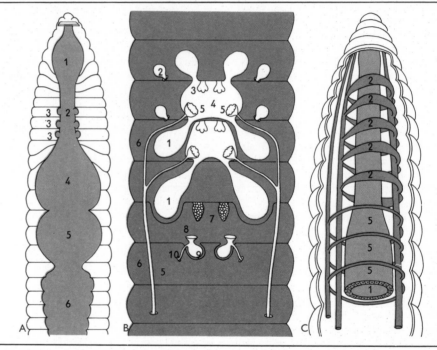

Aspects of a typical earthworm. A. Digestive system: 1. pharynx, 2. oesophagus, 3. calcigerous glands, 4. crop, 5. gizzard, 6. intestine. B. Reproductive system: 1. sperm sac, 2. sperm receptacle, 3. testis, 4. testic sac, 5. sperm funnel, 6. sperm duct, 7. ovaries, 8. egg funnel, 9. egg sac, 10. oviduct. C. Principal blood vessels: 1. oesophagus, 2. hearts, 3. median doral vessel, 4. median ventral, 5. segmental vessel, 6. subneural blood vessel.

Below: Earthworm drawing a leaf into its burrow, and (right) copulating.

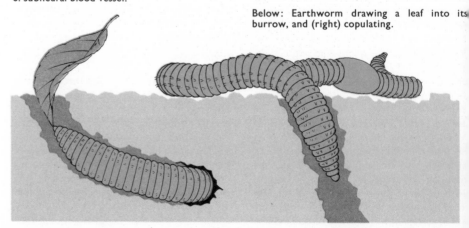

Earwigs showing sexual dimorphism. Female (left) has nearly straight forceps, male (right) has strongly curved forceps.

oxygen-carrying pigment haemoglobin. Circulation of the blood is maintained largely by five pairs of contractile vessels called pseudo-hearts, situated in the front part of the body.

Earthworms are hermaphrodite, each worm producing both sperm and eggs. During pairing, two worms come together, head to tail, and each exchanges sperm with the other. The sperm are stored by each recipient in pouches called spermathecae until after the worms separate. A slimy tube formed by a glandular region, the clitellum, later slips off each worm, collecting eggs and the deposited sperm as it goes, and is left in the soil as a sealed cocoon. In the cocoon the eggs are fertilized, the young worms develop, and eventually escape.

The commonest European earthworms belong to the genera *Lumbricus* and *Allolobophora*. *Megascolecides australis,* of Australia, is enormous, growing up to 10 ft (3 m) or more in length. CLASS: Oligochaeta, PHYLUM: Annelida. A.E.B.

EARTHWORMS' TURNOVER. Darwin's name is always connected with the origin of species but he made important contributions in other topics of biology. In *The formation of vegetable mould through the action of worms with observations of their habits,* he demonstrated for the first time the importance of earthworms in soil formation and, hence, agriculture. The burrows help aerate and drain the soil, the ingestion of soil grinds small particles even smaller and the habit of pulling leaves into their burrows increases the rate of mould formation. Furthermore, secretions from the earthworm's gut lower soil acidity. The effect of these activities on the nature of the soil is immense when one considers the large numbers of earthworms present in the top layers. The population varies with the type of soil but it has been estimated that as much as 25 tons (25 tonnes)

of soil may be raised to the surface as castings over 1 acre ($\frac{1}{2}$ ha) in 1 year. This represents about $\frac{1}{4}$ in ($\frac{1}{2}$ cm) rise in soil level, a factor which is important in the slow burial and preservation of old buildings.

EARWIGS, slender insects, commonly $\frac{1}{2}-\frac{3}{4}$ in ($1\frac{1}{4}-2$ cm) long, with distinctive pincer-like structures at the end of the body (function unknown), comprising the order Dermaptera. If one pokes at an earwig with a finger it may curve its tail over its back and use the pincers (forceps) in a threatening manner. In this attitude it looks rather like a miniature scorpion, but it has no poison and the forceps are not strong enough to hurt. Even so, the appearance is formidable.

The name earwig is probably derived from the fact that it occasionally gets into the ear. This does not result from the insect deliberately seeking out the ear, as some people imagine, but reflects its habit of resting in any suitable crevice into which it can fit. The ear is just another crevice to the earwig. It is also possible, although less likely, that the name comes from the appearance of the hindwing. This is a semi-circular transparent member marked with veins and folds and slightly resembling an ear. The arrangement of veins and folds arises from the fact that at rest the wings are folded beneath the short, leathery forewings and this necessitates transverse folds as well as longitudinal pleating.

Earwigs have jaws which are used for biting and chewing and they seem to eat almost anything. They are of little economic importance, but sometimes they are a minor horticultural pest because some flowers, like dahlias, provide ideal crevices in which to hide. When they are hungry they come out and gnaw holes in the petals, which spoils the flowers from the commercial point of view.

The eggs of earwigs are laid in batches and the young which hatch look like miniature

versions of the adult except that they have no wings and the forceps are straight. Female earwigs are unusual among insects in displaying some sort of parental care over the eggs and young larvae. Usually the female rests over her brood and if the eggs become dispersed she will collect them together again.

There are about 900 species and they nearly all look like *Forficula auricularia,* the common European species. But there are two groups in the tropics which look rather different. Both are parasitic: one, *Arixenia,* on bats in the Indonesian region; the other, *Heminirus,* on Cane rats in Africa. Both are without wings and the eyes of *Arixenia* are very small while *Heminirus* has no eyes. Both are viviparous and *Heminirus* has what appear to be well developed placenta-like structures for the transfer of nutrients from parent to embryo. ORDER: Dermaptera, CLASS: Insecta, PHYLUM: Arthropoda. R.F.C.

EARWIGS AND EARS. Earwig is derived from the Old English *Earwicga* – ear rammer, and its name in other languages is also linked with its being found in ears. In French it is *perce-oreille* and in German *Ohrwurm.* In northern Norway, it is dragonflies that are popularly supposed to crawl into ears hence their name of *Orsnell* – ear snail. Apparently the symptoms of earwigs in the ear, as shown by records in the case-books of medical practitioners, are discomfort and a loud rumbling noise. The cure is to float the earwig out with oil. At one time earwigs were used as a cure for deafness, an example of a common practice in folk medicine of using a cause to cure an effect, as in drinking alcohol to cure a hangover.

ECDYSIS. A number of animals, but notably the arthropods (insects, crabs, spiders), shed the outer layers of their skins periodically in order to grow. This is necessary because the skin, or more correctly in the arthropods the *cuticle, will not expand sufficiently for continuous growth and it has to be replaced by a new skin or cuticle which gives more scope for expansion. The overall process of casting the old skin and replacing it with another is called *moulting, but there is a special name given to the actual shedding of the old cuticle. This name is ecdysis.

It is necessary to have a separate term because sometimes a new cuticle is formed beneath the old one some time before the latter is shed. Perhaps the best known example of this is in a butterfly chrysalis. Quite often it is possible to see the adult butterfly inside and if you break the chrysalis open there is an adult butterfly fully formed with its own cuticle, although very crumpled up. So in a sense this insect has already 'moulted' although it has not shed the old cuticle. In fact, the same sort of thing happens every time an insect or a crab or any other arthropod moults. The old cuticle separates from the cells which made it and a new cuticle is formed; there is then an interval before the old cuticle is shed. Often it is a very short interval, but it is long enough to make it worthwhile having a separate term for the shedding. Another useful term, which is not yet used very much, is apolysis. This refers to the separation of the old cuticle from the cells which formed it.

So at the start of ecdysis the cuticle is already free from the cells beneath. How does the insect or crab then remove it? As the old cuticle separates from the cells its inner layers are digested by enzymes so that it becomes much thinner. Along some lines nearly all the cuticle is digested so that only a very thin layer, the epicuticle, is left and along these lines the cuticle will be very weak. If any pressure is now exerted on the cuticle it splits along these lines of weakness.

What the insect does at the start of ecdysis is to blow itself up by swallowing air or water. Then it pumps blood forwards from the abdomen into the thorax so that this swells up and presses against the inside of the old cuticle. In most insects a line of weakness runs along the middle of the back of the thorax and continues across the crown of the head on to the face. Hence when pressure is exerted the cuticle splits along this line and by huffing and puffing the insect works its thorax and head out. Very often it hangs head down from a branch so it is helped by gravity in the late stages as it pulls the abdomen and legs free of the old cuticle. In this process of ecdysis not only is the cuticle covering the outside of the body shed; the linings of the fore and hind guts and, in insects, the tracheal system are also cast off.

The outer cornified layers of the skins of amphibians and reptiles are also cast off periodically. This process is also known as

ecdysis, although perhaps more commonly as *'sloughing'. In amphibians and some snakes and lizards the whole layer comes off in one piece and it is quite common to find the almost complete skin of a snake. In other cases the skin comes off in large flakes, but in crocodiles the outer layers are worn away progressively, no distinct ecdysis occurring.

R.F.C

ECHIDNAS, also known as Spiny anteaters, are four-legged terrestrial animals, rather like hedgehogs in appearance. They belong to a special subclass of the Mammalia, the Prototheria or egg-laying mammals (see Monotremata). A large echidna is about 18 in (46 cm) long and 8 in. (20 cm) wide, rounded on the back, flat ventrally, and weighs over 10 lb ($4\frac{1}{2}$ kg)—the heaviest recorded weight is 14·3 lb (6·5 kg). The back is covered with hair interspersed with long sharp spines, the underparts, however, are covered with hair only. There is no neck and two hairy holes one on each side of the head serve as ears; a true cartilaginous pinna is present in all specimens but it is difficult to detect since it is buried in the musculature of the head. In some specimens, however, the pinna sticks out beyond the surface of the head to form an external ear. The eyes, found at the sides of the head at the base of the snout, are small and beady; the retina is made up of rods only, which probably enables the echidna to see well in shady and even in dark places. There is a short stubby tail devoid of hairs and spines but there is no scrotum, the testes being internal as they are in reptiles. The morphology of the chromosomes as seen in testis-squash preparations is also reptilian in that large chromosomes and very small microchromosomes can be distinguished. The number of chromosomes in the body cells of the male is 63, in the female 64. There is evidence that the sex determining mechanism of the echidna, and its near relative the platypus, is unique among mammals in that there is no Y *chromosome, the male cells exhibiting only an X chromosome and the females two X chromosomes.

The legs are short and stout, the enormously strong forefeet bearing digits furnished with long spatulate claws. The hindfeet also bear five claws, the second of which is always elongated and is used as a grooming claw. The femur is parallel to the ground and widely everted giving the hindquarters a reptilian appearance. The grotesqueness of its

Ecdysis or the shedding of the old cuticles shown in the Gulf fritillary butterfly *Dione juno*, of South America. Top: the pupa is about to hatch, with the colour of the wings showing through; centre: free from its pupa the butterfly expands its wings; bottom: the emerged butterfly is drying its wings.

Echidna or Spiny anteater of Australia.

appearance is enhanced by the outward eversion of the feet so that the strongly curved grooming claw actually points backwards. The ankle in all males and some females bears a short spur of unknown function. The stoutness and strength of the musculature of the forelimbs is an adaptation for digging in hard earth or breaking up forest litter to expose the ants and termites that comprise their main food, hence the name Spiny anteater.

Apart from their forelimbs echidnas are specialized in other ways for living on ants. The snout is elongated into a beak about 3 in (7·5 cm) long which houses a long whip-like tongue that can be thrust out 6–7 in (15–18 cm) beyond the tiny mouth which is found at the end of the snout. The tongue is smeared with a secretion, of the sub-lingual gland, that has the stickiness and consistency of treacle so that the ants and termites exposed by digging stick to the tongue, which is quickly retracted, with its catch, into the mouth. Once there, the ants are scraped off, when the tongue is thrust out again, against a series of transversely arranged spines on the very long palate. There are no teeth on the jaws, and the ants and termites are pulped by the rubbing action of a set of spines on the base of the tongue against the spines on the roof of the mouth. The homogenized prey is then passed to the stomach but there is no gastric digestion since the stomach is lined with a nonglandular stratified epithelium. However, digestion takes place in the intestine, which is 11 ft (3·4 m) long and this coupled with the slow rate of passage of termites ensures thorough digestion of soft parts. The hard parts of the insects, on the other hand, pass to the exterior virtually unchanged so that the identity of the insects ingested, and their relative proportions in the diet, can be determined by examination of the faeces found in the bush.

There is no separate anus for the passage of the faeces; the urine, reproductive products and the faeces, all passing through a chamber called a cloaca to the exterior. This characteristic, coupled with the fact that the testes are internal, makes it difficult to be sure about the sex of echidnas and the only way to be sure is to palpate the penis which is housed in a preputial sac which communicates with the cloaca through a hole in the ventral surface of that organ. The penis is used for the passage of sperm only, urine passes from the bladder into the urogenital sinus which communicates with the cloaca in both sexes.

There are five subspecies of *Tachyglossus aculeatus*. Some authorities prefer to regard the Tasmanian kind as a distinct species, *Tachyglossus setosus,* since it is geographically isolated, is smaller than the mainland kinds and has a thick woolly coat that

almost obscures the short sparsely distributed spines. The other races of mainland echidnas are distinguished one from the other by such characters as presence or absence of hair on the back, length of the third claw on the hind leg and length and thickness of the spines. The subspecies and their distributions are as follow: *T. aculeatus aculeatus,* Victoria, New South Wales and southeastern Queensland; *T. a. acanthion,* northern and western Queensland and the Northern Territory; *T. a. multiaculeatus,* southern South Australia; *T. a. ineptus,* Western Australia. The validity of these subspecies is uncertain since the numbers of specimens examined are small and the distinguishing characters are merely external anatomical features which doubtless vary considerably.

Echidnas occur only in Australia and New Guinea (for the latter see below). In Australia they live in an extraordinary variety of habitats ranging from the hottest and driest of deserts through humid rainforests to ridges and valleys at an altitude of 5,000–6,000 ft (1,500–1,800 m) in the Australian Alps where the mean air temperatures for the three coldest months rarely rise above freezing.

The first description of the echidna was published in 1792 by the English naturalist George Shaw who received a specimen taken at the newly-established penal colony of Port Jackson in New South Wales. He thought it was a mammal and, since it was covered with spines as well as hair and since it was known to eat ants, that it was related to both the porcupine and the anteater of South America. He called his new mammal *Myrmecophaga aculeata* (*Myrmecophaga tridactyla* is the South American Giant anteater). But it was soon apparent to other scientists that it was no ordinary mammal and that it was very closely related to the platypus. However, it was not until 92 years after Shaw's description that it was realized just how extraordinary these mammals are. On 2 September 1884 two scientists W. Haacke and W. H. Caldwell independently announced that platypuses and echidnas did not give birth to live young but that they laid eggs. Haacke showed an egg in the pouch of a female echidna to the Royal Society of South Australia and Caldwell informed by telegram a meeting of the British Association for the Advancement of Science at Montreal that monotremes are oviparous and that the segmentation of their eggs is meroblastic. This means that the egg contains a lot of yolk, as it does in birds and reptiles, and the cell within the egg sits on top of the yolk. Only during development does this cell and its descendants divide forming a thin cap of cells sitting on a mass of yolk. In other mammals the egg is small and consists only of a cell containing little yolk; during its

development the whole egg cell divides. This is called holoblastic segmentation.

The pouch or incubatorium of the echidna appears on the ventral surface in the female at the beginning of the breeding season which lasts from early July to late September. There is equivocal evidence that the period of gestation in the uterus is 27 days. After this the egg is deposited in the pouch (no one knows how) and is incubated there. The only recorded observation of a successful incubation showed that at a pouch temperature of about 89°F (32°C) this last 10–10½ days. Since the body temperature of echidnas vary from 84°–89°F (29°–32°C) (see below) it is possible that some incubation periods could be longer or shorter than 10–11 days. The pouch egg has diameter of about 0·75 × 0·5 in (16 × 13 mm). At hatching a little animal looking most remarkably like a newborn marsupial breaks out of the egg by means of an egg tooth and attaches itself by clinging with its relatively enormous forearms to one of two milk patches or areolae found on the dorsal surface of the pouch. From the areola it sucks milk secreted by the paired mammary glands which have the many-chambered (alveolar) structure found in the mammary glands of other mammals. The milk, as far as the fatty acid composition is concerned, is very like that of the red kangaroo *Megaleia rufa,* and of the Insectivora. The flow of milk is controlled by a hormone, oxytocin, secreted by the pituitary gland, as it is in domestic mammals. Oxytocin is released in response to the stimulus of sucking and this brings about contraction of tiny muscles around the alveoli which in turn leads to a steady expression of milk. In cows this is known as milk 'let down'. Let down in echidnas enables a 1 lb (450 gm) young to suck in as much as 48 gm milk in less than 30 min. The young echidna remains in the pouch for an unknown period until it starts to grow spines and when the mother cannot stand it any longer she places it in a burrow. She then visits it every one and a half to two days to feed it until it is weaned about three months later; at this time it is roughly 2 lb (900 gm) in weight.

Echidnas are homoiothermic, i.e. their body temperature is largely independent of changes of temperature in the air around them. They regulate body temperature mainly by control of the production of heat but evaporative cooling and vaso-motor processes contribute appreciably to the *temperature regulation. The body temperature at ambient temperatures fluctuates between 84°F (29°C) and 89°F (32°C). This is lower than the body temperatures of most mammals but sloths, for example, have a central temperature of 90°F (32·5°C). As long as echidnas are feeding well they can withstand severe cold down to 41°F (5°C),

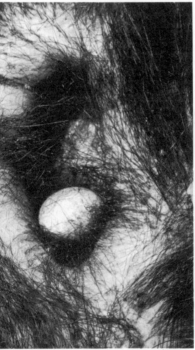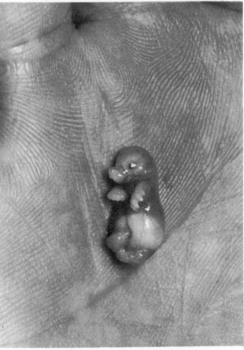

The Australian echidna (top), also called Spiny anteater, one of the egg-laying mammals, showing (bottom left) an egg in the mother's pouch and (bottom right) the newly-hatched baby echidna.

tories of Papua and of New Guinea. The area takes the form of a huge arc running parallel to the Gulf of Papua, extending from Merauke in West Irian through Jimmi and Baiyer River 'Areas in the Western Highlands to Rigo in eastern Papua. *Tachyglossus* has been found within this area at elevations ranging from sea-level to 5,500 ft (1,675 m) in the Sepik-Wahgi Dividing Range.

The island of New Guinea harbours another kind of echidna quite different from *Tachyglossus*, this is *Zaglossus bruijni*. It is a very large echidna growing up to 39 in (1 m) in length and a weight of about 21 lb (9·5 kg) has been recorded. The snout is proportionately much longer than that of *Tachyglossus* and it houses an extremely long tongue. A length of 8·75 in (22 cm) for a tongue preserved in alcohol is given by Van Deusen and George and, doubtless, it was much longer in the living animal. The distal end of the tongue bears a series of cornified or keratinous spines while its base has a knob bearing keratinous teeth for grinding food as in *Tachyglossus*.

The snout, being proportionately very long, is also curved downwards; this characteristic, along with somewhat longer legs, gives *Zaglossus* the appearance of a miniature elephant.

It is found from the eastern part of Papua to the most westerly part of West Irian and apparently on Salawati Island off the west coast of the Vogelkop Peninsula. Its preferred habitat appears to be humid montane forests at altitudes ranging from 3,770 ft (1,150 m) to 9,400 ft (2,865 m).

The food of non-captive *Zaglossus* is not known but the tame animals are very fond of earthworms. They ingest these by grasping either head or tail of the worm, apparently guided only by the tactile sense of the beak, and sucking in the worm. Worms are abundant in the loose humus of the wet mountain forests so it is possible that the two genera have radically different food habits. Nevertheless *Zaglossus* specimens have been known to eat both ants and termites. FAMILY: Tachyglossidae, ORDER: Monotremata, SUBCLASS: Prototheria, CLASS: Mammalia. M.E.G.

ECHINODERMS, marine animals which include starfish, brittlestars, Sea urchins, Sea cucumbers and Sea lilies. The name is derived from the Greek for 'spiny-skinned', but not all members possess this feature. Rather, all modern echinoderms are distinguished by three main characters: a skeleton of plates of mesh-like calcite set within the tissues of the body wall; a basic radial, usually five-fold (pentameral) symmetry of the body; and possession of a water vascular system that gives rise to avenues of tube-feet on the external surface of the animal. These features

but if they stop feeding when kept at low ambient temperatures, the body temperature falls to a little above ambient and they hibernate like many other mammals do. Echidnas, however, are not as good as other mammals at thermoregulation in hot weather; above 95°F (35°C) air temperature the echidna's body temperature rises and it dies of heat apoplexy at about 100°F (38°C). In spite of this echidnas can live in hot deserts where temperatures run as high as 120°F (49°C) in the shade. They do this by avoiding the heat of the day, living in the relative coolness of shallow excavations, the burrows of other animals (fox dens, for example) or in caves; the echidnas emerge from these refuges in the cool of the evening to forage and feed.

Tachyglossus aculeatus also occurs on the island of New Guinea and it is said, on dubious evidence, to be a distinct subspecies *T. aculeatus lawesii*. It was once thought to occur only at Port Moresby and its environs, but largely due to the work of H. Van Deusen and G. George it is now known that it ranges through a large part of the Terri-

Echinoderms

very clearly set the echinoderms apart from all other animals.

Morphology. Where a hard skeleton is present in other invertebrates it is usually an exoskeleton, laid down externally to the body tissues. In the echinoderms, it is an endo-skeleton, that is, formed within the body tissues, in fact, within the mesoderm. This distinguishes echinoderms from most other invertebrates but is a feature they have in common with vertebrates. The structure of the skeleton in echinoderms is that of a three-dimensional network of calcite, quite different from the layered structure to be seen, for example in a mollusc shell. Moreover, it is both surrounded and permeated by soft tissues, which secrete the calcite to form it. Such a structure has three functional advantages: it is relatively lighter and more economical in material than a solid mass of the same dimension; the holes in it provide a means of insertion for the connective tissue which binds the plates together; and the holes may offer a resistance to a force which would otherwise tend to split the plate, for calcite crystals tend to split easily along well-defined cleavage planes and each plate in an echinoderm skeleton (in some species up to 10,000 plates) behaves optically as a single crystal of calcite. For this there is no parallel in other phyla.

Fossil Sea lily *Gissocrinus goniodactylus* from the Silurian rocks of Wales, over 400 million years old.

Rock boring Sea urchin *Paracentrotus lividus*, bores holes in rocks with spines.

All adult echinoderms living today show basic radial, pentameral symmetry, so seems that this feature has some surviva value, for those echinoderms without it soo became extinct. Moreover, it has bee adopted in only one other minor group marine animals, the Priapulida, a group burrowing marine worms.

The water vascular system, a tubula system derived from extensions of the bod cavity (coelom), is perhaps the most funda mental echinoderm character. The syster may consist of about eight main parts: (i) madreporic plate, pierced by very many sma pores, is seen on the upper surfaces starfishes and Sea urchins; it looks superfici ally like a madreporarian coral, hence th name. A similar plate is seen on the lowe surface of brittlestars, but the Sea cucumber seldom possess one; instead there is a internal madreporic body, a swelling pierce by many pores. (ii) A canal, which may b called the stone canal because of the calci spicules imbedded in its wall leads from th madreporite to a circular canal, the cir cumoral water ring, which encircles the gu just behind the mouth. (iii) This water rin distributes fluid from the stone canal to th radial water vessels which radiate from it. I Sea lilies, which have no madreporite, th water ring is itself pierced by pores. (iv

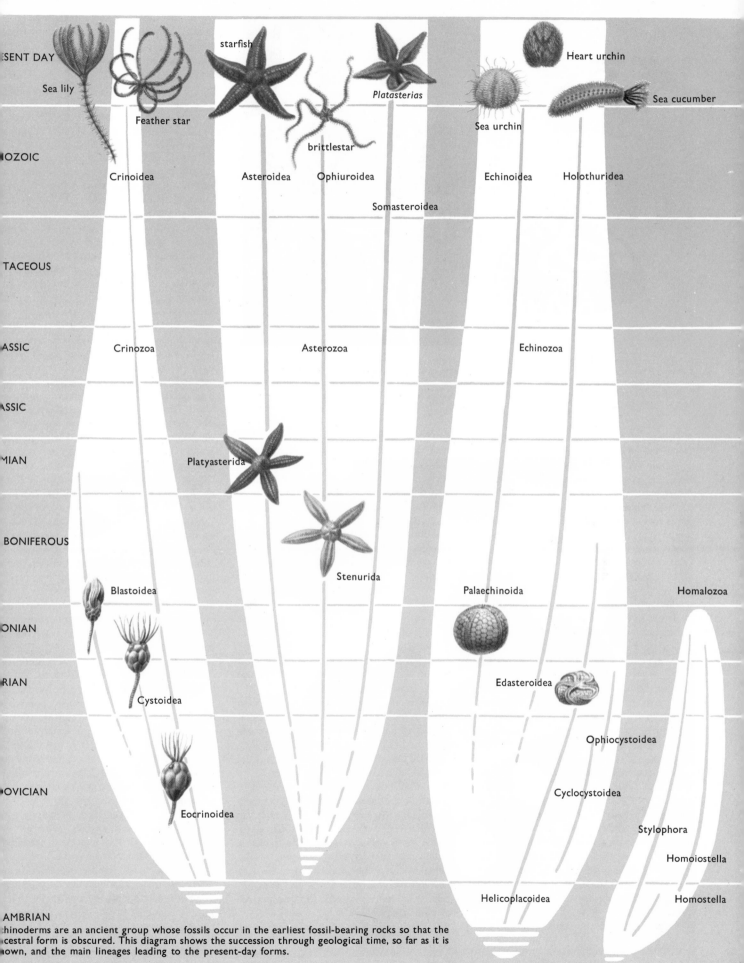

PRESENT DAY

Sea lily

Feather star

starfish

brittlestar

Platasterias

Heart urchin

Sea cucumber

Sea urchin

MESOZOIC

Crinoidea

Asteroidea

Ophiuroidea

Echinoidea

Holothuridea

Somasteroidea

CRETACEOUS

JURASSIC

Crinozoa

Asterozoa

Echinozoa

TRIASSIC

PERMIAN

Platyasterida

CARBONIFEROUS

Stenurida

Blastoidea

Palaechinoida

Homalozoa

DEVONIAN

Edasteroidea

SILURIAN

Cystoidea

Ophiocystoidea

Cyclocystoidea

ORDOVICIAN

Eocrinoidea

Stylophora

Homoiostella

Homostella

CAMBRIAN

Helicoplacoidea

Echinoderms are an ancient group whose fossils occur in the earliest fossil-bearing rocks so that the ancestral form is obscured. This diagram shows the succession through geological time, so far as it is known, and the main lineages leading to the present-day forms.

Echinoderms

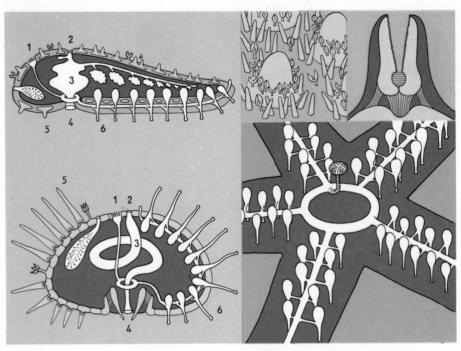

Although outwardly dissimilar, a starfish and a Sea urchin are basically alike in their organization. Above left shows a section through the disc and one arm of a starfish. Below left, a section through a Sea urchin (1. sieve plate, 2. anus, 3. intestine, 4. mouth, 5. calcareous spine, 6. tube feet). Above right, a portion of the surface of a starfish, showing skin-gills among the spines, and (right) a pedicellaria. Below right, part of the water-vascular system of a starfish.

Polian vesicles are muscular sacs, which arise from the water ring. Their function is uncertain, although it has been suggested that they act as temporary reservoirs for fluid when the system is in operation. (v) Tiedemann's bodies similarly branch from the water ring as small sacs, but only in starfishes, where they perhaps produce coelomocytes (see below). Their equivalent is not proved in other echinoderms. (vi) Usually five radial water canals extend from the water ring to carry fluid to the tube-feet; in starfishes the canals lie in a groove on the outside of the skeleton, in Sea urchins and brittlestars the skeletal plates cover the canals. (vii) Tube-feet arise from each canal forming a linear series along each of its sides; the whole structure is called an ambulacrum, from its similarity to a promenade bordered by trees. (viii) Ampullae, muscular sac-like structures projecting into the body from the base of the tube-feet in starfishes, Sea urchins, and Sea cucumbers help to maintain the fluid pressure within the tube-feet.

Since the tube-feet are hydraulic organs, the main function of the water vascular system is to maintain sufficient hydrostatic pressure for their effective operation. Since, however, it is also convenient for several body functions to have a fluid system intermediate between that of the body and the outside sea water, the same system may be put to other uses; it can thus play a part in locomotion, feeding, excretion, sensitivity, and respiration.

Tube-feet are the only echinoderm append-ages found in all living classes, and in many fossil ones. It is difficult to prove their occurrence in the very earliest echinoderms, but there is some evidence that they may have been present. Indeed, it has been suggested that *Tribrachidium*, a problematical fossil from Australian rocks of probable pre-Cambrian age, could have had them and be the oldest known echinoderm although it does not possess a calcite skeleton. If so, and because there are no exact parallels to the system in other invertebrates (although the food-collecting tentacles of some sipunculoids are rather similar), this system may be the most diagnostic feature of the phylum.

Two other tubular systems of lesser significance are also derived from the coelom: the haemal and perihaemal systems. They also radiate from ring-like portions encircling the gut. There is a circumoral haemal ring, with branches extending to the arms, and other ring-like structures encircling different parts of the body in the different classes. Associated with the haemal system in the axis of the body is the co-called axial organ. The functions of both this and the haemal system as a whole are uncertain. Some workers have claimed that the the axial organ, which has been observed to pulsate (as have other parts of the coelomic systems), behaves as a primitive heart. Certainly branches of the haemal system are intimately associated with other body organs such as the gut, so would seem to be concerned with the transport of essential materials.

The perihaemal system, as indicated by its name, normally surrounds the haemal tubes; it may also be associated with the nervous tissues. Its function too is uncertain, but probably similar to that of the haemal system in the transport of materials.

The basic construction of the nervous system is similar to that of the coelenterates. However, since many echinoderms have a large variety and number of moveable parts, for example, the spines in Sea urchins, the system is more highly developed so as to permit rapid transfer of stimuli and co-ordination of movement. There is a circumoral nerve ring and radial nerve cord, similar in arrangement to the tubular systems of the coelom, but also a sensory nerve plexus that lies just below the external surface (epithelium) of almost the entire body, at least in starfishes, Sea urchins and Sea cucumbers (restricted to the tube-feet in brittlestars and Sea lilies since their plates invade the epithelium). Details of the nervous system vary between the classes, being related to their mode of life, particularly style of locomotion.

Distribution. The possession of a water vascular system limits the distribution of echinoderms. Since its membranes are semipermeable, echinoderms cannot live out of water for they then quickly dehydrate and die; members of this phylum are therefore unknown on land. Moreover, since a delicate balance has to be maintained between the salinity of the fluid within the tube-feet and that of the water surrounding them, echinoderms cannot tolerate fresh or even brackish water, apart from a few exceptional species inhabiting slightly brackish waters. Usually echinoderms that stray into such conditions become bloated with excessive water and stunted in growth. They are, however, found in all seas, from tropical to polar, at all depths from the shore-line down to the greatest abysses, and on all types of bottom from abyssal oozes to rocky, turbulent shores.

Although truly abyssal sediments have not been recognized in the rocks of today, it does seem that the broad picture of echinoderm distribution holds true for fossil as well as living forms: they all seem to have lived under marine conditions, and to have flourished best in those environments rich in calcium carbonate which have subsequently been preserved as limestones. It is interesting to note that the dominant echinoderms in Paleozoic seas were all crinozoans, particularly Sea lilies; all other groups are very rare by comparison. In Mesozoic times the Sea urchins became much more numerous both as individuals and species, whereas the Sea lilies, though still important, were less numerous. In Cenozoic times the Sea urchins are the dominant fossils, Sea lilies being rarely preserved. Sea cucumbers, starfishes and brittlestars are much more fragile, so it is

Opposite: a Mediterranean Sea urchin *Sphaerechinus granularis*.

not surprising that their fossil record appears trivial by comparison.

Breeding. Although the eggs, sperm, and very early development of echinoderms have long been subjected to detailed study, relatively little is known of their breeding habits. In general echinoderms reproduce sexually, although a few starfishes and brittlestars can also reproduce asexually by breaking themselves in two, each part then regrowing the missing portion. The sexes are usually separate although a few species are hermaphrodite, but only rarely can the sexes be distinguished externally. Some Sea urchins may rarely show enlarged gonophores in the females; and in a few brittlestars the females tend to be larger than the males. In some species the eggs or young may be brooded by the mother in a special structure, and this serves to distinguish the sexes.

Classification. There are five distinct groups, comprising over 5,000 species, living today making up the phylum Echinodermata; they are usually defined formally as classes:

1. Crinoidea: Sea lilies and Feather stars. Sea lilies are sedentary with a stalk of calcite plates or ossicles supporting a cup-shaped body, the cup or theca formed by regularly arranged calcite plates imbedded in the body wall. The upper surface is covered by a membrane which may contain calcite plates: it has a central opening for the mouth, another to one side of this for the anus; a ring of well-developed, moveable, food-gathering arms bearing tube-feet fringes the upper surface. Feather stars are simply Sea lilies that have adapted to a mobile form of life and do not possess a stalk.

Sand burrowing Sea urchin, the Sea potato *Echinocardium cordatum.*

2. Asteroidea: starfishes. Mobile, star-shaped, with the central body produced into arms, usually in fives or multiples of five. There is no clear structural distinction between body and arms: both contain parts of the vital organs: the arms are otherwise hollow, and each bears a groove on its lower surface containing a radial water canal from which the tube-feet arise.

3. Ophuroidea: brittlestars. Mobile, star-shaped with a central disc-like body surrounded by five (rarely more) radiating arms of distinct structure. The vital organs do not normally extend into the arms, which are bony in appearance with a solid axis of articulating calcite plates; the radial water canal which gives issue to the tube-feet lie beneath the lower arm plates, not in an open groove.

4. Echinoidea: Sea urchins, Heart urchin and sand-dollars. Mobile, with a spherical heart-shaped to flattened disc-like body enclosed in a skeleton or test of calcite plate which bear spines. The five radial water canals of the water vascular system lie within the test and give issue to tube-feet through pores in the covering test plates.

5. Holothuroidea: Sea cucumbers. Mobile, cylindrical or sausage-shaped, usually with only a thick, leathery skin in which are set separate plates of calcite variously shaped as rods, hooks, anchors, or wheels. Modified tube-feet form a ring of tentacles around the mouth; others may emerge via the body wall from five radial canals lying longitudinally within the body.

It was at one time thought that all the mobile, free-moving echinoderms were more closely related to each other than to the fixed Sea lilies, and they were accordingly grouped in a subphylum Eleutherozoa: free-animals distinct from the subphylum Pelmatozoa: fixed animals which contained the Sea lilies and the similarly stalked or sessile fossil forms. Knowledge of the fossil record at that time indicated that fixed forms were in existence earlier than the free-moving species, suggesting that the free forms evolved from the earlier fixed ones.

With increased knowledge of fossil forms it became clear that free and fixed forms are of equally ancient origin, both ranging back to early Cambrian times. Now, four subphyla are recognized, distinguished on the basis of general body form:

1. Crinozoa. Forms of generally static sedentary habit, often fixed by a stem, and having a mouth and anus both on the upper surface, which bears food-collecting arms. Eight distinct classes have been recognized but only one, the Crinoidea (Sea lilies and Feather stars), has survived to the present day. Most of the others have been extinct for at least 200, sometimes 500, million years. Because of this, and because some of them are represented only by very rare specimens, it is quite probable that their classification is unnatural.

(a) Crinoidea (Time range: Lower Ordovician to Recent). The Sea lilies and Feather stars, by far the most abundant and important class and the only living crinozoans. At times in the past they were so abundant that their

The starfish *Marthasterias glacialis* regenerating four arms from the original disc (body) and one original arm, a condition commonly called the 'comet' form.

remains aggregated to form rocks. At the end of the Paleozoic they became much less numerous.

(b) Cystoidea (Range: Lower Ordovician to Upper Devonian). Fossil forms characterized by special pores which pierce the skeletal plates; the plates are irregularly arranged in the earliest members, which thus show radial symmetry only in their food grooves; there are food-collecting arms of distinctive, biserial plate-structure. Although never so abundant or diverse as the crinoids, cystoids were nonetheless an important group in Paleozoic seas.

(c) Blastoidea (Range: Silurian to Permian). These have a distinctive arrangement of the skeletal plates, in four cycles, together with structures termed hydrospires. The earliest of them are similar to cystoids, so may have evolved from them.

(d) Eocrinoidea (Range: Lower Cambrian to Middle Ordovician). A very mixed assemblage possessing neither the thecal pores characteristic of cystoids, nor the feeding-arm structure of crinoids. Yet since there are general resemblances, and the eocrinoids appear earlier in time than the other two, they may include their ancestral stock.

(e) Paracrinoidea (Range: Middle Ordovician only).

(f) Parablastoidea (Range: Middle Ordovician only).

(g) Edrioblastoidea (Range: Middle Ordovician only).

(h) Lepidocystoidea (Range: Lower Cambrian only).

The rare fossils placed in the last four classes are imperfectly known, but seem to be distinct from other crinozoans.

2. Asterozoa. Free-moving, star-shaped, with no stem or means of attachment, but five or more arms extending radially.

(a) Asteroidea (Range: Lower Ordovician to Recent). The starfishes.

(b) Ophiuroidea (Range: Lower Ordovician to Recent). The brittlestars.

(c) Somasteroidea (Range: Lower Ordovician to Recent). Star-shaped with the arms often petal-shaped, each with an axial skeleton of two columns of plates from which arise laterally directed series of rod-like plates to form the broad-flat arms. This is a small group containing only a few fossil genera and one modern one, *Platasterias*.

3. Echinozoa. Usually free-moving, with a spherical, cylindrical, or flattened disc-like body, never with radiating arms. Seven classes have been distinguished within this subphylum, but only two are living today:

Rosy feather stars *Antedon bifida* (above), Duck's-foot starfishes *Anseropoda placenta* (centre) showing undersurface on left, and *Asterias rubens*, common European starfish.

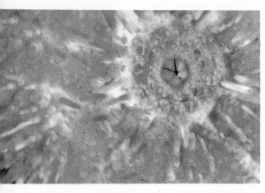

European edible Sea urchin *Echinus esculentus*.

(a) Echinoidea (Range: Middle Ordovician to Recent). The Sea urchins, Heart urchins, and sand-dollars.

(b) Holothuroidea (Range: ? Middle Ordovician, Devonian to Recent). The Sea cucumbers.

(c) Helicoplacoidea (Range: Lower Cambrian). Short, sausage-shaped animals with a spirally plated skeleton of calcite plates. Only recently discovered, the very rare members of this group are amongst the earliest echinoderms known: they demonstrate that the echinozoan stock is an ancient one, but whether they are themselves ancestral to the later Sea urchins and Sea cucumbers is still a matter of conjecture.

(d) Edrioasteroidea (Range: Lower Cambrian to Lower Carboniferous). Small, often disc-like, the upper surface bearing both a mouth and anus and five characteristic food grooves radiating from the mouth; skeletal plates between the distinctive plated food

Oral region showing peristome, mouth, teeth, spines, tube-feet, pedicellariae. Pentacrinoid larva of Rosy feather star *Antedon bifida*.

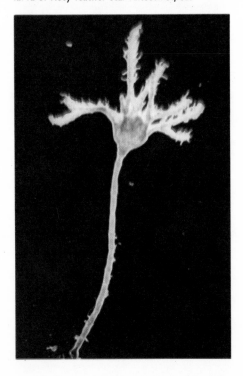

grooves are often irregularly arranged. Because their food grooves in shape and structure resemble those of starfishes, it was once thought they were ancestral to the starfishes.

(e) Ophiocystioidea (Range: Lower Ordovician to Upper Ordovician).

(f) Cyclocystoidea (Range: Middle Ordovician to Lower Silurian).

(g) Campostromatoidea (Range: Lower Cambrian). The fossils placed in the last three classes are structurally distinct from the others, but very rare indeed.

4. Homalozoa. Asymmetrical, flattened, the plates on the two flat sides of the body (theca) differing from each other: a stem (in Homostelea) or arm-like process (in Stylophora) or both (in Homoiostelea) extends from part of the body, being of quite different structure in each of the main groups. All are extinct. There are three classes:

(a) Stylophora (Range: Middle Cambrian to Middle Devonian).

(b) Homostelea (Range: Middle Cambrian).

(c) Homoiostelea (Range: Upper Cambrian to Lower Devonian).

These are rare fossils, so different from other echinoderms that their place in the phylum has been questioned, yet they possess a skeleton of plates of mesh-like calcite and apparently a food groove system similar to that of other echinoderms, both features characteristic of this phylum.   E.P.F.R.

ECHIUROIDS, rather ovoid or bulbous worms of uncertain classification. They may be considered as a class of the phylum Annelida (the ragworms, earthworms and leeches), but it is rather more satisfactory to place them in a phylum of their own, the Echiuroidea, or Echiurida. All are marine, living in rock crevices or burrowing in the sand. They show affinities with the annelids in having a planktonic larva called a trochophore and in possessing chaetae (spiny outgrowths of the body wall). There is often only one pair of chaetae, however, whereas annelids generally have a much greater number. Another annelid feature, segmentation, disappears as the echiuroid becomes adult. Echiuroids have a proboscis used in feeding. In *Bonellia* this is mobile and very long, extending to 2 ft (60 cm), whereas in *Echiurus* or *Thalassema* it is spoon-shaped.

Bonellia lives in rock crevices in sublittoral regions of the warmer seas. The extensible proboscis of the female, bifurcated at the tip, explores the surrounding rocks removing the algal film, which is conducted back along the proboscis to the mouth by the action of innumerable cilia beating in an ordered fashion. The males are minute ciliated worms which live within the segmented organ of the female. Ten or more may live within each female, fertilizing the eggs as

they pass towards the exterior, a remarkable example of sexual dimorphism. For many years it was thought that sex in *Bonellia* was determined by environmental factors; that a larva settling in a vacant crevice would become a female whereas one encountering an adult female would enter her and become a male. It is now known that this is not so and that sex is determined by normal genetical inheritance.

Another unusual feature of *Bonellia* is the green pigment, bonellin, which gives the animal its colour. This is a breakdown product of the chlorophyll taken in with the algal food and proves toxic to a wide variety of invertebrates if placed in their water in the laboratory. Furthermore, bonellin is toxic to *Bonellia* itself, markedly so in the presence of light. It is, therefore, not surprising that

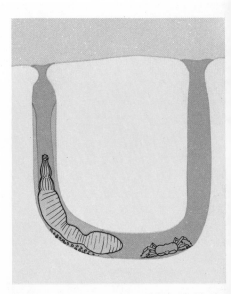

Urechis, a burrowing echiuroid from California, commonly found on the mudflats. Food is collected by means of the slime tube and both slime and food are ingested. It is called 'innkeeper' because of the 'guests' that live in its burrow.

Bonellia avoids the light, living in crevices and at depths where light is meagre.

Urechis is an example of an echiuroid which lives in sand. It inhabits a U-shaped burrow and feeds by straining particles out of the water through a conical mucous bag, the necessary current for this being maintained by peristaltic waves of muscular contraction. These trap small volumes of water between the wall of the body and that of the burrow, passing them along the tube. The hind-gut is very thin-walled and is periodically inflated with water, presumably for the respiratory uptake of oxygen and release of carbon dioxide.

Most known echiuroids live in fairly shallow water, but with recent increased dredging in the deeper seas a number of new species have been discovered. PHYLUM: Echiuroidea.   A.E.B.

ECHOLOCATION, the perception of objects at a distance by animals that generate their own sounds and evaluate, with their own ears, the properties of the echoes reflected back by the objects. This mechanism of perception is found among animals that move freely and rapidly in three-dimensional space, where vision, smell or touch are of little use. Thus it is met with among bats, some cave-dwelling birds, and members of the whale family, including dolphins and porpoises. The marine mammals often swim very actively at great depths where very little light penetrates; most, in fact, is lost at about 100 ft (30 m) below the surface. The sounds animals use in echolocation usually contain very high frequencies that extend well above man's range of hearing. High frequency sounds give sharper echoes or 'sound images' and because of their small wavelength are reflected back by smaller objects than are low frequency sounds.

Echolocation of a quite simple kind occurs in the Whirligig beetle *Gyrinus*, which swims very rapidly on the surface of ponds and rivers. The surface waves that it generates in swimming are reflected back from the bank and are detected by the insect's antennae, part of which floats on the surface film. If the antennae are amputated or damaged the beetles collide repeatedly with the bank.

As long ago as 1793, the Italian biologist, Spallanzani, found that bats could navigate around obstacles even when blinded, but if a transparent hood was put over the bat's head it could no longer avoid obstacles. A contemporary, Jurine, then found that bats would collide with obstacles if they were deaf, but any suggestion that bats used their ears in some undetermined way in navigation was ruled out by the influential French scientist, Cuvier, who proclaimed that the experiments indicated that the animals had a highly developed sense of touch. It was not until an English physiologist, Hartridge, published a report in 1920, that it was suggested that bats orientated by producing sounds at or above the higher frequency limit of man and could detect and respond to the echo. In 1938, the Americans, Pierce and Griffin, acting on Hartridge's theory, tested bats with a newly-developed apparatus that could detect sound with frequencies of up to 100,000 cycles per second, and found that the bats did indeed emit ultrasonic cries while in flight. Subsequently experiments by Griffin and Galambos showed that the Little brown bat *Myotis lucifugus* could navigate a maze of wires of only 1·2 mm in diameter, but only if its hearing was unimpaired and the mouth was not blocked.

The sound that the Little brown bat produces is a series of clicks, each lasting 1–5 milliseconds and having a frequency of around 50,000 cps. The repetition rate of the clicks increases greatly when a bat is ap-

Bats provide some of the best examples of the use of echolocation in the animal kingdom, both for navigating in the dark and for finding the insects on which they prey.

The ear of the Long-eared bat, clearly showing the earlet (tragus) and the many folds in the ear itself which assist in direction finding.

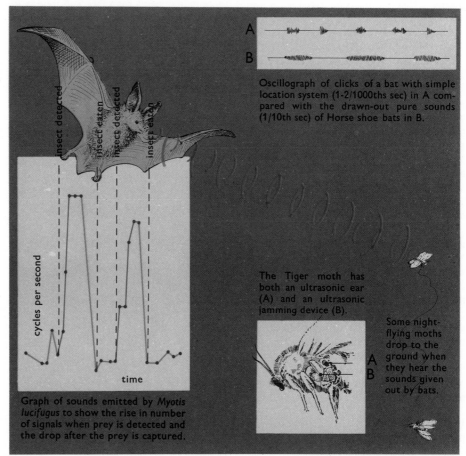

insect detected insect eaten insect detected insect eaten

cycles per second

time

Graph of sounds emitted by *Myotis lucifugus* to show the rise in number of signals when prey is detected and the drop after the prey is captured.

A
B

Oscillograph of clicks of a bat with simple location system (1-2/1000ths sec) in A compared with the drawn-out pure sounds (1/10th sec) of Horse shoe bats in B.

The Tiger moth has both an ultrasonic ear (A) and an ultrasonic jamming device (B).

Some night-flying moths drop to the ground when they hear the sounds given out by bats.

A
B

proaching its prey. Clicks of the Big brown bat *Eptesicus fuscus* are emitted at about 10 cps in cruising flight, but speed up to a crescendo of about 200 cps just before the capture of prey, and the duration of each pulse also shortens. The intensity of bat cries is extraordinarily high; measured a few inches from the mouth of the Little brown bat it reaches 60 dynes per cm^2, which may be compared with intensities of 3 dynes per cm^2 near a pneumatic drill and 25 dynes per cm^2 in a noisy boiler shop. It is perhaps fortunate that the upper limit of our hearing is not higher, or the peace of many summer evenings would be shattered.

The Brown bats belong to a family of European and New World bats known as the Vespertilionidae. These produce a click which undergoes a substantial drop in frequency while it lasts, and is emitted through the mouth. The Horseshoe bats (Rhinolophidae), on the other hand, produce pulses of a more or less constant frequency and emit them through the nose. The pulses are longer than those of vespertilionids and the frequency is usually higher, reaching 100,000 cps in some species. The ears are typically large and are kept in a rapid vibratory motion during flight. The mechanism of echolocation therefore appears to be different in the two families, but in both it is believed to involve the perception of beat notes generated by the interaction of the emitted sound and the echo. (Beat notes are heard as rhythmic intensity changes when two notes of slightly different frequencies are sounded together.)

Not all species of bats use echolocation, and some species that tend to fly rather slowly, such as Fruit bats and Vampire bats, produce very weak sounds. The Fish-eating bat *Noctilio* is known to use echolocation in catching fish. For a long time it was a mystery how it was able to do this, for nearly all the sound energy is reflected off a water surface, but it has now been shown that it can detect objects that break the water surface, and even a wire protruding 1 mm can be detected.

Bottle-nosed dolphins *Tursiops truncatus* produce two main kinds of sound; whistling noises and series of rapidly repeated clicks. Both contain frequencies of up to 170,000 cps, but it is the clicks that serve in echolocation and are emitted more or less continuously by the animals. Experiments have shown that the dolphins can distinguish between fishes of different sizes by listening to the echoes from them, and that they can find their way in the dark through a steel mesh curtain, avoiding gaps blocked with transparent plexiglass.   P.E.H.

ECLIPSE PLUMAGE, a dull post-breeding plumage adopted by the males of certain species of birds, particularly the ducks (Anati-

dae), in which a bright breeding dress is replaced by a sombre, usually cryptic plumage similar to that of the female. Eclipse plumage is also found in the bee-eaters (Meropidae), cuckoo-shrikes (Campephagidae), sunbirds (Nectariniidae) and weavers (Ploceidae). The primary reason for the eclipse plumage would seem to be to provide camouflage for the survival of the male after he has finished breeding. This is particularly so in those birds, such as ducks, which are flightless during the post-breeding moult.

ECOLOGICAL NICHE, one of the most fundamental concepts in modern ecology, and perhaps in biology as a whole. Unfortunately it is to some extent an abstract concept and, because the biologist's understanding of this aspect of ecology is changing rapidly, it is a hard one to define. The ecological niche of a species is its way of life, or way of making a living, in the habitat or microhabitat in which it lives.

Broadly speaking, a species requires two things from its environment if it is to survive there. First there must be enough space for the members of the species to live in. That is, there must be enough suitable places for building nests or digging holes, or to provide any other kinds of shelter or 'homes' that the members of the species may require. Secondly, there must be an adequate supply of food. The way in which a species obtains these requirements for space and food is its ecological niche. Ecologists consider the niche of a species to have two components, the spatial component, the habitat or microhabitat in which it lives, and the functional component, the way it obtains its food. A simple analogy is with a man wishing to live

The long-necked gerenuk *Litocranius walleri* lives in dry savannah browsing scattered thorn bushes.

Impala inhabit open bush, never far from trees

in a particular environment, a town or village. He must have both a place to live and a job or profession at which to make a living. Similarly the ecological niche of an animal species consists of its 'home' and its 'profession'.

A consideration of the ecological niches of some familiar animals, such as the big cats, may make the concept more clear. All of the species obtain their food by predation, and all of them take a fairly wide range of animal food, though mostly the prey are large animals, often bigger than the cats themselves; this is the functional component of their niches. All of the species have a distinct geographical range, and within these ranges each species lives in a limited range of habitats, the lion, for instance, occurring in savannah country and the tiger mostly in jungle; this is the spatial component of their niches. All other animal species, from the smallest Protozoa to the largest mammals and birds, have similar preferences for particular habitats and types of food, which together make up the species' niche. The niche of a species is a unique property of that species and of that species alone.

Species of animals vary greatly in the 'width' of their ecological niche: that is, in the number of different habitats they can live in and types of foods they can use. The 'broader' the niche of a species the more environments in which it can live. Many insects, for example, aphids and some butterflies and moths, have very 'narrow' niches because they are dependent for food on particular plant species and frequently the foliage or stems of the food plant also form the species' microhabitat as well. Such 'specialist' species are often very efficient at utilizing the resources of food and space that their niche provides, and they may become very abundant where these resources occur; most agricultural pests are 'specialists' with narrow ecological niches. In contrast many other species, which might be termed 'generalists', are much more flexible in their requirements for space and food and consequently are often very widespread. Many of the species of irds that have succeeded in colonizing urban environments (such as the European starling *Sturnus vulgaris*) are species of this type. Generalists' are probably less efficient at using their wide range of resources than are the 'specialists' in using theirs and in general, although widespread, do not become so abundant. Some very common species, the starling and the feral pigeon *Columba livia* for instance, are exceptions to this rule, but the success of many of these is largely influenced by man. In fact our species, *Homo sapiens,* is a good example of a species with a broad ecological niche. We are omnivorous, using a wide range of both animal and plant food, and as a result of our ability to make clothes and shelters we can live in all but the most extreme environments.

There are two important extensions to the concept of the ecological niche. The first is the theory that two species of animal cannot share an ecological niche, or at least not the whole of it. This theory was originally derived from experiments carried out since about

Giraffe can feed from tall trees.

1930 by several ecologists, of which the Russian biologist G. F. Gausse was one of the first. In these laboratory experiments two or more animal species, usually closely-related and believed to have very similar, or identical, ecological niches, were forced to live together in a small, rather simple environment. Different species of Protozoa, especially *Paramecium,* in test tubes of culture medium, species of small Crustacea (*Daphnia*) in flasks of water, Flour beetles (*Tribolium*) in small vials of flour, or species of Fruit flies (*Drosophila*) in glass bottles, were all used at various times for these experiments. In most cases the experimenters found that after a period of time only one of the species survived in the environment provided. This suggested that the species were unable to share these limited resources of space and food. In these circumstances one species was always more efficient in exploiting the resources offered so that its population grew fastest and eventually monopolized all the available resources of

food and space. In a few of the experiments the two species both survived in the environment. Further analysis showed that in these cases the species were either occupying different parts of the environment or were using different food resources. In other words, the species had created two ecological niches out of the environment.

For·many reasons experiments like these are hard to interpret, particularly if we wish to use the results to explain the ecology of natural populations of species. But the experiments have given rise to what is called the Principle of Competitive Exclusion which suggests that it is impossible for two species populations to continue for any length of time to occupy the same ecological niche. Probably most, but not all, ecologists would now agree that this suggestion is probably correct, and the experimental evidence for it is not completely convincing either way. In the analysis of the ecological niches of natural populations of species it has nearly always been found that species with very similar food requirements tend to occupy different parts of their environment, or alternatively that species living closely together tend to utilize different foods. All of which supports the hypothesis that species do in fact have distinct and unique ecological niches which they do not usually share with other species.

The second extension of the niche concept is the theory that environments, or habitats, contain only a limited number of ecological niches, or ways of making a living. Since only one species can occupy each niche, the number of species (species diversity) that can live in the habitat is also limited. The main evidence in favour of this hypothesis is that different parts of a *biome in roughly the same latitudes tend to have not only similar numbers of species, but also similar types of species, apparently occupying much the same range of ecological niches. For instance, the grassland biome in different parts of the world seems to include niches for one or two species of large herbivore, such as the bison in North America, wild horses in Eurasia, the Pampas deer in South America, several species of antelopes, gazelles and zebra and eland in Africa and the kangaroos in Australia. These species are not closely related taxonomically, which emphasizes that in different circumstances in different geographical regions very different species may evolve to occupy an available niche; such groups of species are called *equivalent species. Similarly, there seems to be a niche in grassland for a smaller mammalian herbivore, often burrowing, and able to crop short turf already grazed by larger mammals. This niche is filled by the European rabbit, Jack rabbits of North America, Ground squirrels and jerboas in different parts of the biome.

Many different factors act together to determine the number of ecological niches

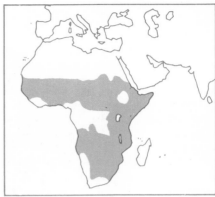

The lion's habitat is savannah with scattered trees or open woodland: Africa, southern Asia.

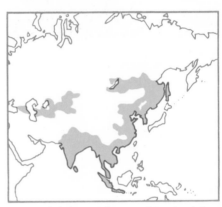

The tiger's habitat is forest and jungle: Asia.

The leopard's habitat is varied, from rocky areas with scattered vegetation to forest: Africa, southern Asia.

The puma's habitat includes a wide variety of terrain, from mountain forest to grasslands: N and S America.

The Amazon river in Brazil and its tributaries form a low, tropical valley, sparsely populated but rich in plant and animal life.

available in a biome or habitat and therefore the species diversity of the habitat. During *ecological succession habitats increasingly develop greater complexity of structure as more and more plant species of greater size enter the system. The later stages of succession as the climax is approached usually contain many more species than earlier ones, and so it seems that structural complexity is one factor determining the number of available niches. Consequently woodland habitats provide many more niches and have many more species than grassland habitats. Another factor is the *productivity of the habitat, that is the total amount of plant and animal material that it contains and that is added to it each year. Generally tropical habitats have much higher productivity than temperate ones and tend to have more niches and therefore more species than comparable temperate habitats. For instance, whilst woodlands in Vermont have about 80 species of birds of 65 genera breeding in them, woodlands in Panama (tropical rain-forest), about 600 miles (1,000 km) north of the equator, have about 175 species in 121 genera. The high species diversity of tropical regions probably has several causes. One is certainly the high rate of productivity within them, which makes plenty of food available and therefore enables species to survive in smaller ecological niches than in temperate regions where food resources are more thinly spread.

The concept of the ecological niche, then, relates to the very fundamental ecological problems as the Principle of Competitive Exclusion and the number of species that may live in a habitat. This is an area of very active research work and many of the ideas discussed in this article are very likely to be modified or abandoned altogether in the future.   I.N.H.

ECOLOGICAL PYRAMIDS, express the relative numbers, biomass or contribution to energy flow of the various trophic levels of an ecosystem (see particularly the entry on food chains and webs).

ECOLOGICAL SUCCESSION. Over a period of time there are changes in both the numbers and types of plants and animals which live together as the biotic community of an *ecosystem. This process of change is called ecological succession and this is one of the most important concepts in ecology. Naturalists have known since the 17th century that the vegetation of an area frequently changed, but the first serious studies of these processes, involving animals as well as plants, were by F. E. Clements, H. C. Cowles, V. E. Shelford and C. C. Adams around Lake Michigan during the first 40 years of this century. Many of their ideas were developed from studies of sand dunes around the lake. Strong winds blow the sands of the beach into dunes; these are very unstable until they are invaded by various species of grass which can put down deep roots and stabilize the dunes. As the dunes get more firm and dead grass fertilizes the sand with organic matter, less hardy plants invade the dunes and, later, shrubs such as Sand cherry, dogwood and juniper. These provide enough shelter from winds and frosts for the establishment of trees, particularly cottonwood and pine. The trees form a canopy which reduces the amount of light reaching the soil surface and because of this the grasses and small plants which were the 'pioneers' of this 'developing ecosystem' are eliminated. The pine trees shed their needles onto the soil and build up its humus content. This encourages invasion of the pine forest by oak and hickory trees which eventually replace the pines. Finally, about 150 to 200 years after the formation of the dune, a forest of beech and sugar maple trees develops and this is the final stage of the succession. At least seven quite distinct communities or associations of plant species, each dominated by one or two prominent species, can be recognized at various stages, and these can be seen in a sequence passing back inland from the lake shore. Several thousand species of animals are involved in this succession, but because they are mostly small, are less obvious. Each of the seven plant communities has a distinctive animal community living in it and dependent on it for food and shelter. For instance, there are 54 species of Orthoptera (grasshoppers, crickets, Stick insects and roaches) present and six or seven of these are found in each plant association, though some of them live in two or three neighbouring plant communities. Many other animal groups, amongst which ants, spiders (of which 228 species are involved), beetles, birds and snakes are especially prominent.

A similar succession of species, involving animals and plants related to those found around Lake Michigan, can be seen on sand dunes in other parts of the world. Many other ecosystems show similar phenomena. A well known example is the sequence of communities found in ponds and small lakes as they dry out. At first the community is dominated by floating plants but as the water becomes more shallow plants rooted on the bottom emerge at the surface and, gradually, a terrestrial community, dominated by trees, develops. A sequence of communities like this, or the one found on dunes, is called a sere, and the individual communities are seral stages. Generally each sere ends in a type of community which is less subject to change than earlier ones and may be more or less permanent. This is called a climax community and it is considered that at this stage the ecosystem is fulfilling its potentialities with the energy and nutrients that are available to it. One sere that has been thoroughly studied in recent years is very common in North America, the 'old field' succession.

Over the last 200 years or so many areas of farmland have been abandoned by their owners in parts of the eastern and southeastern United States. In the first year or two after the last crops of cotton or corn are removed the land is invaded by weeds and grasses which eventually form a close carpet. During the following 20-odd years this is invaded by tough grasses like broomsedge, and by shrubs. This community is replaced over 100 years by pine forest, which beneath its canopy shelters many shrubs and, in the later stages, seedlings of oak and hickory. These seedlings grow up through the pines and shield them from light so that they are eliminated, and after 150-200 years a climax vegetation of oak and hickory forest is reached. The ecologist E. P. Odum has studied the sequence of communities of passerine birds that inhabits this 'old field' sere, in the Piedmont region of Georgia.

A large number of species of birds make their nests in this sequence of plant communities, but only about 10% of these can be regarded as common. There is an early peak in number of species after about 20 years; this is because the plant community contains a large number of species at this time (that is, it is very 'diverse') which provide many different sources of food and nest sites. In the early stages of pine forest which follow many of these plant species are eliminated because of shading by the fast-growing trees, and, consequently, there is also a fall in the number of bird species present. Later numbers recover because the mature pine and oak forests provide plenty of food and nesting sites.

This 'old field' sere illustrates a number of important principles of ecological succes-

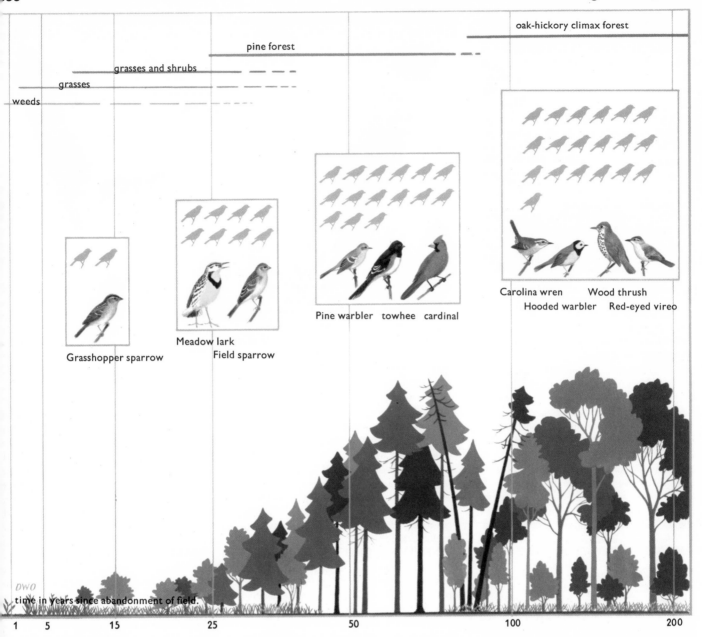

oak-hickory climax forest

pine forest

grasses and shrubs

grasses

weeds

Grasshopper sparrow

Meadow lark
Field sparrow

Pine warbler   towhee   cardinal

Carolina wren   Wood thrush
Hooded warbler   Red-eyed vireo

time in years since abandonment of field.

1   5   15   25   50   100   200

Ecological succession is shown here by a schematic representation of the change from a meadow to woodland over a period of 200 years. Changes in the kinds of birds inhabiting the area are indicated, as are the numbers of individuals. The combined changes in total amount of vegetation and animals represent changes in the biomass.

sion. First the number of species in the biotic community increases very rapidly in the early stages of succession, in this case from 15 to 136 species of birds in the first 20 years. Typically, as in this case, the rate of increase in the number of species present slows in the later stages as the climax community is reached. As well as number of species, the size of the major plant species and some of the animal species also usually increases, especially in terrestrial situations, so that the *biomass, the total amount of living material present, increases too. The total quantity of living matter in forests may often be as much as 200 to 400 thousand kilograms per hectare, whilst the quantity in the grasslands that preceded the forests may

be only two or three per cent of this. The amount of non-living organic matter present in the ecosystem, most of which is humus in the soil, also increases during succession. A consequence of the increase in biomass and of the number of species between which it is divided, the feeding relationships of the organisms in the ecosystem, the *food chain or web, becomes much more complex.

In contrast to these factors, the net productivity of the ecosystem, the amount of new material added by growth each year (see productivity), decreases during succession. This is because as the biomass of the system increases the proportion of the energy incorporated by the plants which must be used to maintain the metabolism of the system in-

creases, leaving less available for growth. This is the reason why most of the ecosystems which we use for agriculture are very early stages of succession, bare soils (arable) and grasslands (pasture); these stages have high productivity and we can obtain the biggest crop of energy and materials from them.

One of the more interesting aspects of ecological succession is that it is largely predictable, and that ecosystems in similar situations but widely separated geographically, such as sand dune systems of the eastern United States and of western Europe, tend to follow much the same sequence of communities in succession, though the species involved are usually different. Within a geographical area the relatively stable climax community reached at the end of a successional sequence in very different ecosystems may be very much the same. In both eastern North America and western Europe succession in most ecosystems, whether sand dunes, small ponds or abandoned farmland, mostly ends naturally in some kind of deciduous forest, containing oaks, with hickory or maple in North America, and beech or sometimes ash in Europe. Most parts of the world have particular types of climax vegetation terminating most successions, and this is probably related to the particular climate of the area; the climate of the eastern United States and western Europe, cool temperate with year-round rainfall, seems to favour deciduous woodland (see biomass).

Processes of succession can also be seen in units of the environment smaller than the whole ecosystem. Rotting branches on the forest floor, for instance, have a sequence of communities of fungi, bacteria, insect larvae, Protozoa, nematodes and earthworms, which succeed each other over periods of 10–20 years after the dead branch falls from the tree. On a much shorter time scale of three to six months, cowpats are colonized, and consumed, by many different invertebrates, with communities specialized to live in the conditions provided by all the stages of breakdown of the dung. In the laboratory ecologists have been able to grow simple 'model' ecosystems, such as small aquaria, in which succession of communities to a climax can take as little as three weeks.
I.N.H.

ECOLOGY, the study of the relationships between all types of organisms and their environment. The term, originally 'oecology', came into use in the 1880's and is derived (like the word 'economy') from the Greek word *oikos* which means a house or a home. Biologists now recognize that organisms are so closely integrated with both the living and non-living components of their environment that the two must be studied as a single functioning unit. So a modern definition of ecology might be 'the study of the structure and function of nature'.

ECOSYSTEMS, a concept suggested originally by the English ecologist Sir Arthur Tansley in 1935. Earlier ecologists had found that characteristic communities of organisms, that is, biotic communities, were associated with particular habitats. Tansley realized that the community was not only dependent on its habitat but also, through the phenomenon of *ecological succession, largely creates it and continuously modifies it. The community and its habitat are therefore two components of a single system which Tansley

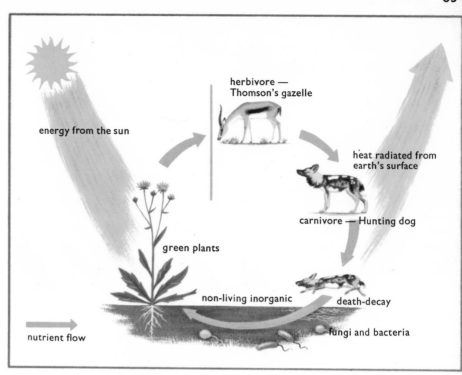

The components of a typical ecosystem.

called the ecosystem. Neither component can exist without the other; if the animals and plants are removed the habitat disappears.

Organisms invading a new environment such as bare sand on a sand dune, or boulder clays left by a retreating glacier, are pioneer species which immediately begin to modify the conditions so that other less 'pioneering' organisms can enter the community that develops. Mosses and grasses add organic matter to the soil and increase its fertility, which may permit small shrubs and, later, trees to invade. These small plants also provide shelter and food for animals which in turn are the prey of others, so that as time goes on the community includes more and more animals and plants, each modifying and forming part of the habitat for all the others. The bare soil or sand that was the environment of the early colonizers has given the community the basic mineral materials or nutrients for its growth and water, the air above has provided it with atmospheric gases, and sunlight has given it an energy source, but the other properties of the habitat, its form, structure and *microclimate have been the creation of the community itself, so that the two cannot be separated.

Ecosystems are real things which can usually be recognized quite easily: a pond, a forest, a field of grass, or an ocean. They vary greatly in size, but all share certain principles and processes. The most important of these is that the plants and animals within them have a pattern of feeding relationships called the *food chain or web. The green plants of the ecosystem incorporate mineral nutrients, energy from the sun and carbon dioxide into

their tissues to form organic compounds which provide the food resources of the whole ecosystem. They are called the 'producers' of the system. All the other organisms (animals, bacteria, fungi) obtain their supplies of energy and mineral nutrients from green plants or each other and are termed the 'consumers' of the system. The energy which the plants take in is used up by the ecosystem and is radiated from the world's surface as heat. The nutrients, on the other hand, are broken down by specialized organisms (decomposers: fungi, bacteria and some animals) and return to the soil where they can be incorporated again by green plants (see biogeochemical cycles). Thus energy enters the ecosystem as sunlight and leaves it as heat, whilst nutrients circulate constantly between the producers, consumers and decomposers and their habitat. These two processes of energy flow and nutrient circulation are a common property of all ecosystems and involve both the biotic community and their non-living environment. Precisely the same principles apply in ecosystems which man controls for his own purposes, such as agricultural ones; the only difference is that the rates of flow of energy and the direction of circulation of nutrients are controlled by man.

Despite these similarities there are many different types of ecosystem, which differ in the size and type of organisms which form their biotic community. The extremes of the range of ecosystems are 'open water' communities found away from the shore, in the sea and large lakes, and land communities such as forests. First these differ in the basic

aw materials' presented by the habitat. In
e aquatic community all mineral nutrients
d atmospheric gases are dissolved in water
d energy in sunlight must pass through
ater to reach the community; to remain
ating together as a community the organ-
ms must be lighter than water or have
echanisms that will increase their buoy-
cy. The land community obtains its
trients from the soil (though they are often
ssolved in water in the soil) and its gases
om the air and energy passes through the
mosphere to reach the community; plants
n root themselves firmly in soil but must
pport themselves in air. Consequently the
ganisms forming the 'open water' com-
unity are mostly small single-celled plants
hytoplankton), small animals (zooplank-
n) and fish, but are usually very numerous.
n land the plants tend to be much bigger
ith heavy, skeletal structures for supporting
emselves in air (trees and shrubs) or grow
ose to the surface of the soil where they need
tle support (mosses, grasses); the animals
e often larger (mammals, birds, insects) but
e generally much less numerous. For the
imals the supporting framework for the
stem is provided by the substance of the
bitat: by water in the aquatic system, but
other organisms, the plants, and by soil
d air in the terrestrial system. All other
osystems such as estuaries, smaller bodies
water, sea and lake shores and grasslands,
e in these respects intermediate between the
pen water' and the forest ecosystems.

Ecosystems do not function independently
each other. There is considerable exchange
both nutrients and energy between them by
igrating animals, windblown vegetation,
aterials in flood water and so on. This has
d some people to suggest that the ecosystem
merely an abstract concept and that all
osystems are just loosely demarcated
visons of one big ecosystem, the whole
orld or the *biosphere. There is some truth
this but the concept is a useful one for the
actical ecologist. In any case, ecosystems
ry greatly in their degree of isolation from
e influence of others, from small ponds
hich may be little more than wetter exten-
ons of surrounding ecosystems to the centre
large forests and the open water of oceans
hich are far removed from other eco-
stems.   I.N.H.

CTODERM, the outermost germ layer of
embryo. In forms where only two germ
yers are recognizable, for example, in
elenterates, the ectoderm gives rise to the
ter cell layer of the adult and is still
nerally referred to as the ectoderm. In
nbryos in which three germ layers can be
cognized, as in all multicellular animals
cept sponges and coelenterates, it gives rise
the epidermis and most sense organs as
ell as the nervous system.

ECTOPARASITES, parasites which live on
the outside of their hosts, either temporarily
or permanently. Temporary parasites, such
as Vampire bats and mosquitoes, have few
adaptations for parasitism except for an
ability to find the host and feed on its tissues;
in these instances, sharp mouthparts to
penetrate to the blood system. Permanent
ectoparasites, such as the Fish louse, lice
and fleas, often have flattened bodies and
limbs specialized for clinging. See parasites.

ECTOPROCTA, one of two groups into
which the *Bryozoa, or moss-animals, were
formerly divided, the other being the Entoprocta, now classified as a separate phylum.

EDENTATA, an order containing only
three living families of mammals—the anteaters, sloths and armadillos. Although
Edentata means 'without teeth', only the
anteaters are completely toothless. Both
sloths and armadillos are equipped with
primitive peg-shaped cheek or grinding teeth
(molars) that are simply blocks of dentine
that lack enamel. True incisors, canines and
premolars (bicuspids) are absent in all edentates, but Two-toed sloths have four specialized molars that resemble and act like
canines. As a group the edentates are un-
aggressive creatures, living on insects, leafy
vegetation, or a combination of plant and
animal matter. Some, such as the sloths, are
among the real curiosities of the mammal
world. Although differing greatly in their
peculiar habits and bizarre appearances, the
sloths, anteaters and armadillos are highly
specialized for, or adapted to, particular
kinds of lives, and all have their roots or
origins in pre-Pleistocene South America.
They are among the handful of living mammals whose ancestors were some of the very
earliest South American mammals. Thus,
present day edentates are exclusively inhabit-
ants of the New World—ranging from
Kansas, Missouri and the Gulf states to
Patagonia.

The ancestors of our modern edentates
date back to the late Paleocene epoch of the
Tertiary period—some 60 to 70 million
years ago—when mammals were just beginning to appear. A few of the early edentates
developed in North America, but the great
majority of species evolved on the southern
continent where they flourished during the
60 million years South America was an
isolated island. Most are now extinct, and the
edentates are a waning group.

The armoured edentates (armadillos) and
the hairy forms (sloths and anteaters)
diverged far back in their geological history.
Whereas most of the early armadillos did not
differ greatly in form and habits from their
living relatives of today, one group called the
glyptodonts (meaning 'sculptured-tooth') had
a solid shield of armour similar to the cara-

pace or top shell of a turtle. It is thought that
early man may have used these big shells as
shelters, for at the peak of their evolutionary
development glyptodonts were as much as 8
or 9 ft (2·4 or 2·7 m) long. Some also had
heavily spiked tails resembling war clubs and
were undoubtedly formidable and imposing
looking beasts. Far more diversity occurred
in the prehistoric hairy edentates. Common
ancestors of today's anteaters and tree sloths
were the ponderous ground sloths. These
ancient sloths all appear to have been strictly
ground-dwelling leaf-eaters, and most were
bear-sized. But the largest, the Giant ground
sloth *Megatherium,* was as big as a modern
elephant—its skeleton alone measuring over
15 ft (4·5 m) in length.

With the rising of the Panama land bridge
connecting North and South America, about
2 or 3 million years ago at the end of
Tertiary times, animals were able to migrate
and greatly extend their original ranges.
Numbers of kinds poured south, but the
isthmus was a two-way street, and some of
the early edentates moved north. Thus,

The Lesser anteater *Tamandua tetradactyla,* the
size of a cat but with long head and tail, carries
its single young one on its arboreal hunt for ants.

skeletal remains of ground sloths and glyptodonts have been found in the United States. The ground sloths reached as far north as Pennsylvania and Illinois. Fossil evidence indicates clearly that these old edentates existed when man began to populate the Western Hemisphere. Exactly why the glyptodonts and ground sloths became extinct is still unclear, but by the end of the Pleistocene, 20,000 to 30,000 years ago, they, along with many other mammals, such as the mastodons and mammoths, had all disappeared.

Only three species of true or edentate anteaters (family Myrmecophagidae) exist today—the Giant anteater *Myrmecophaga tridactyla,* the tamandua or Collared anteater *Tamandua tetradactyla,* and the Silky, Least or Two-toed anteater *Cyclopes didactylus.* All have elongated tapered snouts (good for poking into rotting logs and anthills) with tiny tubular and toothless mouths. The tongue is long, thin, very flexible, and covered with sticky saliva, ideal for probing crevices and picking up small insects. The forefeet are equipped with heavy curved claws, and because of them, anteaters walk on their knuckles or edges of their

Six-banded armadillo *Euphractus sexcinctus.*

palms with the claws turned in. The foreclaws are formidable defence weapons when necessary, but their primary function is to rip open the hard-walled nests of termites on which anteaters mainly feed. Anteaters range from southern Mexico through Central America to Paraguay. The Giant anteater is terrestrial and found principally in the savannahs or open grasslands of northern South America. But both tamanduas and the tiny squirrel-sized Silky anteaters have prehensile tails and spend most of their lives in the trees of tropical forests. Giant anteaters are apt to be awake and active during the day as well as at night, but tamanduas and silkies are basically nocturnal in habit. The Silky anteater gets its name from its soft buff-grey to golden fur. It is the least known anteater, being difficult to locate in the wild and seldom surviving long in captivity. By day it sleeps curled in a tight little ball in a tree

Two-toed sloth in classical posture hanging back downwards from a branch.

hollow or forked branch, and then forages at night for tree-nesting ants and termites. When frightened, this quaint little creature holds tightly to a branch with its grasping tail and hindfeet. Then drawing upright, it holds its forefeet close to its face, and in this defence position it looks most appealing. However, strong quick downward blows with its sharp foreclaws can inflict painful gashes.

Famed for their upside down, almost sedentary existence, the sloths (family Bradypodidae) are actually extremely well adapted to their tree-dwelling way of life. Peacefully feeding mainly on leaves, shoots, tender twigs and fruits, they have little need for speed, agility or sharp eyesight, and their main protection from predators is their dense coat of coarse hair, tough skin, ability to curl into an almost impenetrable ball and general inconspicuousness. In the rainy seasons, green algae cling to the sloth's grooved hairs, enhancing its protective camouflage. When pressed, however, sloths slash out with their powerful arms equipped with long curved claws. So adapted are sloths for tree life that they are exceedingly awkward and almost helpless on the ground. In trees, they seldom hang suspended only by their hook-like claws for very long periods. Rather, they prop themselves in branches with their backs well supported. The sloths are found in tropical forests from Honduras south through Brazil and Paraguay to northern Argentina. There are two basic genera, the

Three-toed sloths or ais *Bradypus,* with three toes on each foot, and the Two-toed sloth *Choloepus,* having two toes on the forefeet and three on the hind. The kind most often seen in zoo collections is the Two-toed sloth for the Three-toed is exceptionally difficult to keep. Two-toed sloths, however, are hardy animals and have been known to live 13 to 15 years.

Armadillos (family Dasypodidae) are the only living mammals with a bony armour. About 20 different species exist today ranging from southern Kansas, Missouri and Florida south to Patagonia. They vary in size from the Giant anteater *Priodontes giganteus*—5 ft (1·5 m) or more in length— to the tiny 5 in (12·7 cm) Fairy armadillo or pichiciago *Chlamyphorus truncatus.* All have some degree of protective shell or armour, remarkably modified skin in horny bands or plates that provide the hard covering over the back, sides, tail and head. Softer flexible skin between the plates permits movement, and the number of the narrow bands across the back is often a handy way of identifying different species and gives some their common name, such as Three-banded, Six-banded and Nine-banded armadillo. Only a few of the armadillos can roll themselves into a tight ball to protect the soft underparts. Their typical reaction to danger is to rapidly disappear into their burrows or speedily dig themselves out of sight in loose soil. Whereas sloths and anteaters usually give birth to a single baby, in the armadillo olyembryony (the division of a single ferti-ized egg that results in the production of two r more identical young) commonly occurs. For instance, the Nine-banded *Dasypus rovemcinctus,* typically gives birth to quad-uplets. At birth baby armadillos are covered with soft leathery skin that gradually ardens into the characteristic armour of the pecies. Armadillos have many small peg-ke molar teeth, among the most primitive ound in mammals. The teeth usually num-er from seven to nine in each half of the aw, and they grow throughout life. Arma-illos are ground-dwellers, great diggers, and re usually found in open areas. They live on nsects, other invertebrates, small verte-rates, plant material and carrion. ORDER: identata, CLASS: Mammalia.   M.M.W.

ELPOUTS, a family of blenny-like marine ishes related to the Wolf eels. They are ound in the cold northern waters at all epths ranging from the low-tide mark to more than 5,000 ft (1,650 m). Their common ame is derived from their eel-like shape oupled with the word pout, possibly a de-ivative of the Old Dutch *putt* or toad, a eference to their toad-like head. The dorsal nd anal fins and the tail are continuous to orm one fin round the body. The pelvic fins re greatly reduced and lie in front of the ases of the pectoral fins. Many species of elpouts give birth to live young.

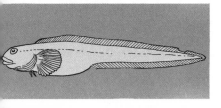

typical eelpout.

The eelpout or Viviparous blenny *Zoarces viviparus* of European shores is frequently ound hiding under stones or weeds on the hore when the tide has receded. Like the utterfish or gunnel, this species has only a ingle ovary instead of the paired ovaries ound in most fishes. Fertilization is internal nd the eggs are attached by small processes o the ovary walls. They hatch in about 20 ays but remain for a further three months nside the mother and the fry are $1\frac{1}{2}$ in (4 cm) ong when they are finally released. During hat time they receive nourishment from ecretions from the walls of the ovary. A emale of 8 in (20 cm) may bear 20–40 oung, while a large fish may bear up to 300. he eelpout grows to about 16 in (40 cm) in ength.

The largest of the eelpouts is an American

lvers 'roping' up rocks. Even adult eels show emarkable dexterity in climbing.

Atlantic species, *Macrozoarces americanus* which reaches $3\frac{1}{2}$ ft (105 cm) in length. This species is not viviparous but lays large eggs, $\frac{1}{4}$ in (6 mm) in diameter, which are guarded by one or both parents. FAMILY: Zoarcidae, ORDER: Gadiformes, CLASS: Pisces.

EELS, elongated fishes belonging to two suborders of the large order Anguilliformes, namely the Saccopharyngoidei or Gulper eels and the Anguilloidei, which contains all other families of eels. Eels lack pelvic fins and were formerly placed in a large group, the Apodes (meaning 'no feet') which, how-ever, contained a number of non-eel-like fishes included because of the absence of pelvic fins. Characteristic of the eels is the long body and the long dorsal and anal fins which are joined to the tail fin to form a single long fin. Pectoral fins are usually present but the bones supporting them have lost the connection with the skull usually found in the bony fishes. As a result, the pectorals are often distant from the head and the gill apparatus and branchial region of the head are elongated. The long and narrow branchial or gill chamber is used as a pump to force water over the gills and out of the sometimes small gill opening. Some species have smooth, naked bodies while in others there are small but deep-set and irregularly scattered scales. There are very many verte-brae, normally 1–200 but sometimes as many as 5–600, and the sinuous body is extremely flexible. This eel-like form, which is found in certain other bony fishes not related to the eels, is nearly always associ-ated with a bottom-living, burrowing or crevice-dwelling mode of life. In most of the burrowing eels the fins are reduced or lost and the tail may become hardened to

become a digging tool. Eels are often rapaci-ous feeders and the jaws and teeth are well developed. Common to all the eels is a thin, leaf-like larval form, the leptocephalus stage, from which the eel metamorphoses into the adult after a few months or even after two or three years. The muscle segments or myomeres of the leptocephalus not only re-main constant in number when the adult form is attained, but also equal the number of vertebrae. The muscle segments are easily counted in the leptocephalus, while the verte-brae can be counted by dissection or X-ray in the adult. Since the numbers of vertebrae are often characteristic of the species, this provides a most useful clue to identifying the leptocephalus larvae of different species.

The eels are clearly a highly successful group. Modern classifications recognize 23 families of eels together with three families of Gulper eels. There are over a hundred genera and several hundred species. The best known family is the Anguillidae, which con-tains the freshwater eels, but the three largest families are the Congridae (Conger eels), the Ophichthidae (Worm eels) and the Muraenidae (Moray eels), the two latter essentially tropical in distribution and char-acteristic of coral reefs. Eels are essentially warm water species with a distribution that coincides with that of the tropical, shallow-water corals (i.e. bounded by the 68°F (20°C) isotherm). Some species have, how-ever, penetrated into subtropical and temper-ate waters but return to warmer waters to breed. Probably all eels require a tempera-ture of at least 65°F (18°C) and a salinity of 35 parts per 1000 in order to spawn, even though the adults may live in colder and less saline waters.

The Common freshwater eel of Europe

Two Common European eels among seaweed. Male eels stay nearer the coast than females.

Anguilla anguilla has long intrigued scientists. It is extremely abundant, found often in foul conditions and quite capable of moving over land on dark nights. The great mystery, however, was where this eel breeds since adult females with eggs inside them had never been found. Aristotle, the Father of Zoology, noticed this and thought that eels emerged spontaneously from the 'entrails of the earth'. Pliny thought that young eels came from pieces of adult eels that had been scraped off onto rocks. The hairs from horses' tails were another supposed source of eels and even as late as the last century a small silver beetle was believed the parent of eels. Aristotle had noticed, however, that large eels went down to the sea and that small eels came back up the rivers.

For centuries eels have been caught for food and in that time countless millions have been cut open without anybody noticing the ovaries and testes (hard and soft roe). Then in 1777 Professor Mondini of the University of Bologna announced that he had discovered a female eel with immature eggs in ovaries with frilled edges lying along the top of the abdominal cavity. In 1788, Spallanzani of Padua University, an excellent observer and the first to investigate the way bats find their way in the dark, reported on his observations on eels. He noticed how determined the adults were to escape from traps

and continue their journey to the sea and he concluded that they were obeying a blind instinct that was probably connected with breeding; he also confirmed that small eels came back from the sea. Spallanzani was not wholly convinced that Mondini had found the ovaries of an eel since he estimated that 152 million eels had been cut open from Lake Commachio and not one contained an ovary. The search for the reproductive organs of eels continued and a century later, in 1874, a Polish zoologist, Syrsti, found testes in a medium sized eel and for a long time the search for testes was confined to the larger eels (it is now known that the males are substantially smaller than the females and rarely grow to more than 20 in/50 cm).

The question was not fully resolved until 1897 when Grassi and Calandruccio had the great fortune to capture a sexually mature female eel in the Straits of Messina and were able to confirm that Mondini had indeed found a female, although it had been immature. In 1903 a male with ripe gonads was found off Norway. Thus, one half of the problem was solved. Eels clearly laid eggs and must mature and spawn in the sea. But still no eels smaller than the 6 in (15 cm) elvers that ascend rivers had been recognized.

In fact, the larval stage of the eel had already been described. In the 1770's a small

fish resembling a transparent willow leaf h. been found by Mr William Morris in the s near Holyhead. He sent it to the great Briti naturalist Thomas Pennant who published description of it under the name *Lep*. *cephalus morrisii* in his *British Zoolog* Pennant believed it to be a distinct speci related to the Moray eels. Once again, lu enters the story. In 1896 Grassi a Calandruccio were working in the Straits Messina when they caught two of the leaf-like leptocephali. They kept them ali in an aquarium and to their very gre surprise saw them sink and change into t shape of miniature eels. It was fortunate th they caught leptocephali that were on t point of changing into eels. Since then t name leptocephalus has been given to all fi larvae of this transparent willow-leaf type.

There remained one important proble Where did the European freshwater e spawn? From the turn of this century shi constantly took samples of the animal life the Atlantic and Mediterranean and it w found that in the latter the largest lept cephali were at the eastern end and th smallest at the Atlantic end. The search the Atlantic intensified and it was found th smaller and smaller leptocephali were foun as the searchers went westwards. T Johannes Schmidt goes the credit for final finding the spawning grounds of this eel. F plotted the lengths of the leptocephali ar the position where they were found ar produced a map of the Atlantic with co centric circles which centred on the Sargass Sea, between 20° and 30° N and 48° and 6: W. In this area were found leptocephali only 10 mm, the smallest yet found.

It would seem that the detective story w. completed. In 1959, however, Dr Den Tucker of the British Museum (Natur. History) put forward a radically differe theory to that of Schmidt. He agreed that th little leptocephali must drift across th Atlantic some 3,000 miles to Europea shores, but he pointed out that very fe adult eels have been caught in the sea and a of these have had the alimentary canal s constricted that they could not possibly fee Tucker decided that the adult eels coul never survive this tremendous journey with out food and that they must die. In that cas how was the species maintained? Tucke concluded that the parents of European eel were the American freshwater eels *Anguill. rostrata*. The two species are very simila differing mainly in the number of vertebrae the European eel having an average of 11 and the American eel 107. Tucker pointe out that there is good experimental evidenc that the numbers of body parts (vertebrae fin rays, etc.) are higher in individuals th embryonic development of which has taker place in lower temperatures and vice versa The colder part of the Sargasso Sea has a

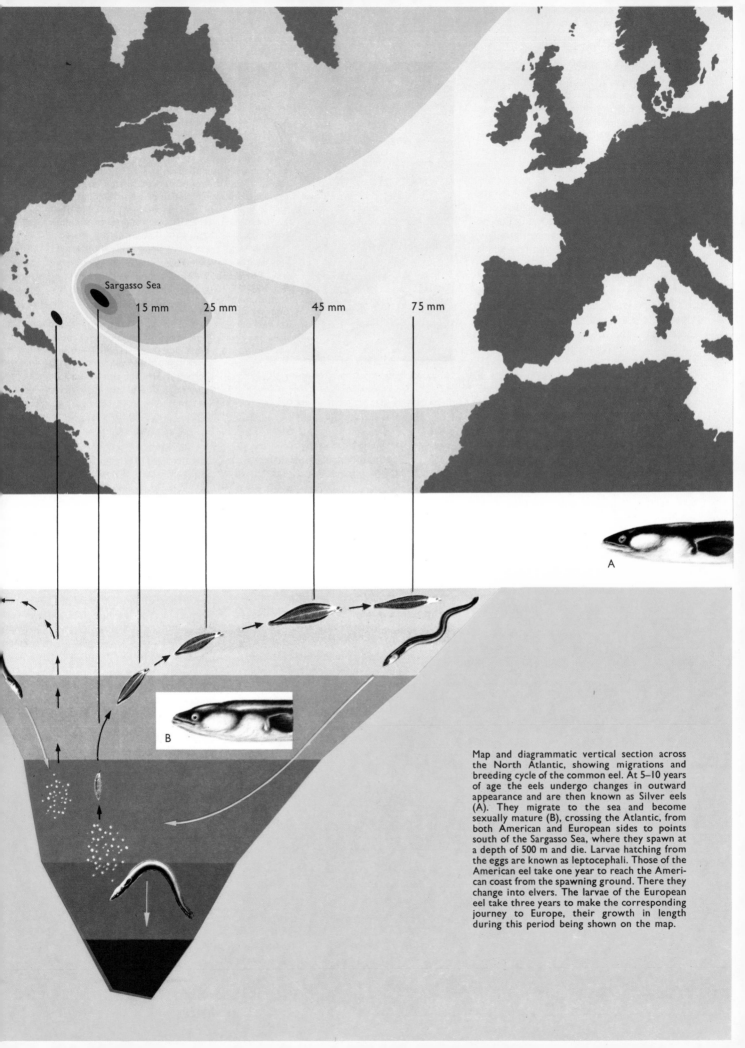

Sargasso Sea

15 mm   25 mm   45 mm   75 mm

A

B

Map and diagrammatic vertical section across the North Atlantic, showing migrations and breeding cycle of the common eel. At 5–10 years of age the eels undergo changes in outward appearance and are then known as Silver eels (A). They migrate to the sea and become sexually mature (B), crossing the Atlantic, from both American and European sides to points south of the Sargasso Sea, where they spawn at a depth of 500 m and die. Larvae hatching from the eggs are known as leptocephali. Those of the American eel take one year to reach the American coast from the spawning ground. There they change into elvers. The larvae of the European eel take three years to make the corresponding journey to Europe, their growth in length during this period being shown on the map.

northwest current which could drift larvae towards European coasts and their development would be at a lower temperature than that of the larvae drifting to the American coasts. Hence the two species of eel were really one and the European stocks were entirely maintained by adult American eels which had a much shorter journey back to the spawning grounds.

Thus the story which began with Aristotle 2,000 years ago is still not fully understood. Until an eel that has been marked in Europe is found near the spawning grounds, Tucker's theory must stand as a reasonable alternative explanation.

Anguillid eels are found in other oceans and their biology is similar, the young elvers ascending rivers and the adults passing down to the sea and probably spawning in deep water. They live in the rivers of Southeast Asia and Japan, southeast Australia and New Zealand.

In older natural history works two sorts of eel were described from Britain, the Yellow eel and the Silver eel. It is now known that the Silver eels are those about to migrate to the sea and a similar silvering is found in eels from other countries. The slime of the eel, that helps to prevent desiccation during the eel's overland journeys, also contains a mild poison, ichtyotoxin, to which some people are allergic should it enter cuts on their hands.

Members of the Congridae, the Conger eels, are like the anguillids in that they have colonized temperate waters but must return to warmer waters to breed. The Conger eel is described elsewhere.

The Garden eels, of the family Heterocongridae, are plankton-feeders. They live in colonies in fine coral sand, excavating a tube in the sediment by means of the tail and sinking out of sight if danger threatens. A colony of these fishes resembles a garden of waving spindly plants.

The Moray eels (family Muraenidae) from

Moray eel *Rhinomuraeana amboinensis.*

the Mediterranean and tropical oceans are large naked eels with mottled bodies that often live in holes in coral or rocks. One species, *Thyrsoidea macrura,* is reported to reach 13 ft (4 m) in length. These fishes are very voracious and were much admired by the Romans; Vedius Pollio was said to have kept a pond of morays into which recalcitrant slaves were thrown. Morays, which are good to eat except for a few extremely poisonous species, are much more colourful than the anguillids. The American Atlantic moray *Gymnothorax funebris* is a beautiful yellow-green in colour; *Muraena helena* from the Mediterranean and the Atlantic is brownish with yellow-ringed irregular brown blotches. The genus *Echidna* from the Indo-Pacific region contains eels that have flattened, grinding teeth instead of the more usual biting teeth and many species are highly coloured.

The family Cyemidae contains deep-sea Snipe eels. *Cyema atrum* is found in all tropical and temperate oceans at depths below 6,000 ft (2,000 m). The jaws are slender and elongated like the beak of an avocet and the dorsal and anal fins are separated at the tail. This species, which grows to 6 in (15 cm), has a short and deep-bodied leptocephalus.

The Snipe eels (Nemichthyidae) are elongated, deep sea eels with long and slender jaws that curve away from each other at the tips. The body tapers to a point. *Nemichthys scolopaceus* grows to about 5 ft (153 cm) and lives at depths of 1,500–6,000 ft (500–2,000 m) in the tropical Atlantic. It breeds in the Sargasso Sea and the leptocephalus is worm-like. The slender jaws, which cannot close at the tips, would seem to be a hindrance but analysis of stomach contents shows that these fishes feed on

crustaceans. The deep-sea eels of the family Serrivomeridae also have long jaws that cannot be closed at the tips.

The Snake eels (family Ophichthyidae) are tail-burrowers with sharp and spike-like tails and most species lack pelvic fins so that the body is a simple unimpeded cylinder. About 200 species are known, mostly small, less than 3 ft (90 cm), and many are brilliantly coloured.

The Worm eels (family Moringuidae) are also burrowers but appear to enter the sand head first. These species are worm-like, with one lip (usually the upper) often overlapping the other.

The eels are an example of a group of animals that have exploited the possibilities of a particular body feature (elongation) and have successfully used it in conquering a wide range of habitats. The fossil history of the group is fairly well known. One fossil, a moderately elongated eel-like fish in which the pelvic fins are still present (absent in all modern eels). Another fossil, from 60 million year old beds at Monte Bolca in Italy, is so well preserved that the brown pigmentation is still clearly visible.

One feature of eel behaviour which arises directly from the elongated form, and the powerful muscle system associated with it, is their skill in climbing. This has been noted in the freshwater eels. They will climb banks of rivers to travel overland, so can find their way from rivers to lakes, thereby widening the range of water they can use. Even dams are no obstacle, whether these include a sloping face of concrete or a brick wall. An eel, migrating upriver, will swim at such an obstruction, lunge at its face and, half jumping, half-wriggling, pull itself up. If unsuccessful at the first attempt it will persist, trying again and again until it has achieved this first step. When the obstruction is made of bricks, the eel will exploit every crack, crevice or hole, using the head and tail alternately to scale the wall. ORDER: Anguilliformes, CLASS: Pisces.

EEL GIANT. The discovery of the migration of the leptocephalus larva by Johannes Schmidt took about 20 years of careful gathering of data. Not only were larvae collected by the Danish research ships *Thor*, *Margarethe* and *Dana* but Schmidt also enlisted the help of merchant ships crossing the Atlantic. An unusual find in one of the *Dana*'s trawls was a 6 ft (1·8 m) leptocephalus. Since the 3 in (7·5 cm) larva of the freshwater eel may grow to a 4 ft (1·2 m) adult, a 6 ft larva suggests an adult 60 ft (18 m) or more in length. Such an eel has never been seen, unless it was the origin of some of the sea-serpent stories.

Colourful Moray eels resting in a drainpipe.

ELWORMS, colourless, transparent micro-
opic worms that live in soil, decaying plant
animal matter, fresh or salt water, or as
rasites in plants or insects. They are usually
orm-shaped with a thick superficially ringed
ticle. Most eelworms are only $\frac{1}{100} - \frac{1}{25}$ in
·2–1·0 mm) long but a few are $\frac{1}{5} - \frac{2}{5}$ in (5–10
m) or longer. Some have elaborate cuticular
ocesses on the head but never true append-
es on the body. The body wall has four
ngitudinal muscle bands. There is a nerve
g with associated ganglia round the hind
d of the muscular pharynx. The excretory
stem consists of longitudinal canals leading
a ventral excretory pore in the front third of
e body. Sex organs in females consist of
ngle or paired ovaries, spermatheca, ovi-
ct and uterus leading to a vagina and
ntral vulva: males have one or two testes
d a pair of copulatory spicules in the
oaca.

Eelworms are found wherever there is
oisture and organic matter. They inhabit
·ils in all climates, often to a depth of 5–6 ft
½–2 m) in sandy soils. They also live on sea
·ores, in fresh water, sewage beds, vinegar
ts, cardboard beer mats, mosses in the
·rctic, lichens on walls and trees, in mush-
·om beds and the tunnels of bark-boring
·etles, while some are parasites in insects
·d others are parasites in plants. For
·ovement they need water which can be a
·m as thin as $\frac{1}{500}$ in (0·005 mm) such as that
·vering the particles of a moist soil. Some
·rvive desiccation for long periods: coiled,
·iescent larvae of the Stem and bulb
·lworm *Ditylenchus dipsaci* can remain
·able for 20 years in a dry cotton-wool-like
·ass. *Anguina tritici* forms galls or 'cockles'
ears of wheat and may survive in the dry
·lls for 30 years. The encysted eggs of
·st-forming eelworms *Heterodera* also sur-
·ve for many years, whether in moist soil or
·y in tubes. Although some eelworms die in
·oded soil through lack of oxygen, some
·rvive immersion in sea water.

Many eelworms are bisexual but some
·ecies lack males and reproduce by pro-
·ndrous hermaphroditism (i.e. first male,
·en female) or by parthenogenesis. Repro-
·uction is rapid under favourable conditions.
·einura celeris, a soil-inhabiting species that
·eds on other eelworms, has a life-cycle of
·4–60 hours at 82°F (28°C) and females lay
·ne egg every 90 min whereas some species of
·agger and Needle Eelworms, *Xiphinema*
·nd *Longidorus* respectively, take two or
·ree years from egg to adult and have
·nly one reproductive cycle a year.

Some eelworms too feed on small particles
·ch as bacteria by pumping them into the
·outh, while others have hooked teeth
·pposed to rasps and can seize and swallow
·ctive prey. Many have hollow mouth stylets
·ith which they puncture other eelworms or
·lant cells and inject a secretion paralyzing

their prey or partly digesting plant or fungal
cells. They then suck out the contents. In
mushroom beds fungus-feeding nematodes
multiply rapidly and may destroy the mushroom fungus. Without food the fungus-
feeding eelworms dwindle and are superseded
by a rich bacterial flora that is eaten by
bacterial-feeding eelworms such as *Pan-
grolaimus* which in their turn multiply and
decline, making their contribution to the
continuous cycle of growth and decay in the
mushroom compost.

The insect parasite *Mermis* is an eelworm
often seen as a white thread 4–5 in (10–12
cm) long coiling on vegetation after heavy

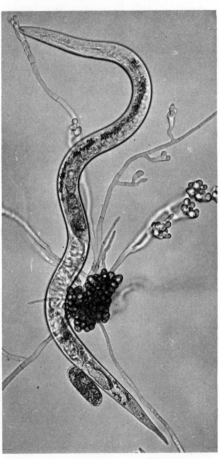

Ditylenchus myceliophagus feeding on *Botrytis
cinerea* mycelium and having recently deposited
an egg.

dew or rain in summer. It attaches hundreds
of eggs to the leaves of plants that may be
eaten by insects such as earwigs or grasshoppers. Inside the insect the eggs develop
into mature eelworms, often killing or steriliz-
ing their host. Eventually the insect falls to the
ground where the mature *Mermis* emerge,
mate and enter the soil. The females coil into a
tight knot and lie dormant for up to two years
to emerge in warm damp weather, lay their
eggs and start a new generation.

Some eelworms are important pests of
crops and much research is being done on
their biology and on ways of minimizing the
damage they cause. Amongst the earliest

recorded species is *Anguina tritici*, shown by
Roffredi in 1775 to be the cause of 'cockles' in
wheat. Shakespeare mentioned the disease in
Love's Labour's Lost (Act 4, Sc 3): 'Sow'd
cockle reap'd no corn'.

The Stem and bulb eelworm, known for
100 years, causes disease in rye, oats, lucerne,
clover, onions, strawberries, narcissus and
tulip bulbs. The plants are stunted and
unproductive and may be killed if invaded as
seedlings. Leaf-blotch eelworms *Aphelench-
oides* cause brown dead patches on leaves of
chrysanthemums and ferns, while a member
of the same genus feeds on the growing points
of rice plants decreasing the yield of grain
(white tip disease of rice). Both this species
and the Stem and bulb eelworm can be carried
in a quiescent state on seeds of their host
plants and thus distributed to new areas. The
Coconut eelworm *Rhadinaphelenchus coco-
philus* is carried by the Palm weevil and
spreads rapidly in the trunk. An infested tree
soon dies and when the trunk is cut it exhibits
a ring of red tissue, hence the name 'Red ring
disease'.

Many eelworms feed on roots, some
harmlessly, others causing necrosis, distor-
tion or galling. With their mouth stylets they
feed on epidermal cells or enter the roots,
move around or settle in one place, and feed
and multiply. Those that wander in the roots
often cause necrotic lesions, moving to fresh
tissues to keep ahead of the dying cells
because they need healthy cells for their food.
The cells fed on by certain sendentary forms
do not die but enlarge and coalesce with
neighbouring cells forming multinucleate
syncytia rich in protoplasm called 'giant
cells'. 'Giant cells' are typical reactions
induced by cyst eelworms and root-knot
eelworms *Meloidogyne*, both having females
that swell enormously and produce many
eggs. Root-knot eelworms cause severe root
galling and are serious crop pests in the
tropics. Some ectoparasitic eelworms feed on
gall root tips which become swollen, hooked
or curly.

Severe losses from eelworms often arise
when crops are cultivated intensively especially on sandy soils. Infested plants often
become more susceptible to other pathogens
and some eelworms transmit plant viruses.
Plant parasitic eelworms that attack one or a
few crops can be controlled by crop rotations.
Crop varieties have been bred resistant to
some eelworm pests, e.g. stem eelworms in
oats, lucerne and clover, cyst eelworms on
potatoes and soya beans and root-knot
eelworms on tomatoes and tobacco. CLASS:
Nematoda, PHYLUM: Aschelminthes. M.T.F.

EELWORM TRAPS. Eelworms living in the
soil face an unusual hazard; that of predatory
fungi. The eelworms are active forms that
thread their way through the soil particles and

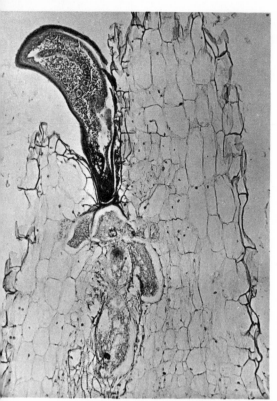

Longitudinal section of root with young female cyst nematode (*Heterodera*), top left, with head embedded in root and adjacent 'giant cells'.

they fall prey to over 50 species of fungi whose hyphal threads penetrate the eelworms' bodies. There are several ways by which the hyphae penetrate the eelworms. Some fungi form sticky cysts which adhere to the eelworm, then germinate and enter its body. Other fungi form sticky threads and networks, like a spider's web, and the eelworms become trapped on them. Some fungi form lasso-like traps, consisting of three cells forming a ring on a side branch of a hypha. An eelworm may merely push its way into the ring and become wedged or the trap may be 'sprung', the three cells suddenly expanding inwards in a fraction of a second, to secure the eelworm. It is interesting that these fungi do not need to feed on eelworms to flourish and they only develop traps if eelworms are present in the soil.

EFT. Old English name for a small lizard it was later used for the Smooth newt and this persists locally for it in Britain, sometimes as effet or evet. In North America it is used for the terrestrial larvae of certain newts. In these the aquatic larval stage changes into the eft which leaves the water and lives on land for as much as three years. It then returns to the water, develops a tail fin and becomes a sexually mature adult. The eft differs from the adult in having a rougher skin and a tail which is not flattened from side to side, and in being a different colour.

In the Red-spotted newt *Diemictylus viridescens,* for example, the adult is olive-green with a few red spots and reaches a length of about 4 in (10 cm). The eft is called the Red eft, is brilliant orange or red and reaches a length of about $3\frac{1}{2}$ in (8·8 cm). The adults live in ponds and ditches in the eastern half of North America while the efts are found sometimes on the forest floor, after rain, in large numbers, making no attempt to remain concealed.

The efts of other species of *Diemictylus* are also reddish in colour.

The eft stage is not always passed through. In some parts of its range a species may transform straight from the aquatic larva to the aquatic adult. None of the European newts has an eft stage. ORDER: Caudata, CLASS: Amphibia. M.E.D.

EGG-EATING SNAKES. The true Egg-eating snakes are adapted to living on eggs that are at least twice the size of the snake's gape. The six species form a subfamily, Dasypeltinae, of the large snake family *Colubridae. Modifications in the structure of these snakes allowing them to engulf, swallow, pierce and crush eggs then regurgitate the shells are to be found in the extreme reduction of teeth, flexibility of the jaws, development of special neck muscles and of long, downward and forward directed spines on some of the vertebrae. These sharp spines, which are tipped with dense bone, penetrate the wall of the gut and form a mechanism for cracking eggs.

Five species occur in Africa south of the

Sahara and in Arabia and belong to the gen *Dasypeltis*. One species, *Elachistod westermanni,* found in northeast India i exceedingly rare; since it has grooved ba fangs and a sensory nasal pit it may not fe exclusively on eggs. All true Egg-eaters l eggs; there may be a dozen in a clutch. A adult 2 ft (61 cm) long *Dasypeltis* can eat chicken's egg four times the diameter of own head. Forcing the egg against a loop its body the snake may take 20 minutes engulf it. Once worked into the throat the e is forced back, then as the snake arches neck the shell is pierced by the spines on t backbone. As the snake moves its neck dov again boss-like processes on the vertebrae front of the spiny ones flatten the egg and means of a valve in the oesophagus t contents are squeezed towards the stoma and the shell compressed into a neat packa is regurgitated. Numerous species of snak augment their diet with eggs but none is highly specialized as the Dasypeltina although some Chinese rat snakes (*Elaph* are fairly similarly modified and one speci at least has vertebral spines penetrating t oesophagus.

In pattern and proportions some species *Dasypeltis* superficially resemble the veno ous Night adder *Causus* and the Saw-scal viper *Echis* and in West Africa and Sudan three may occur together. In warning b haviour too *Dasypeltis* is similar to *Echis* f both employ their rough scales for stridul ting. Generally the keels of the third to fif row of scales along the sides of the body of t African Egg-eater are serrated and in

Newt from North America where the name eft is often used for the adult.

Four stages in the swallowing of an egg by an egg-eating snake.

defence posture the snake coils up in a C-shaped curve, inflates itself and by rubbing the body coils against each other makes a loud rasping noise while simultaneously lunging with open mouth, although not biting the aggressor. FAMILY: Colubridae, ORDER: Squamata, CLASS: Reptilia.   J.S.

EGG PROTEIN. The classification of birds is more complete and stable than that of any other group of animals. This is partly because birds are 'obvious'. They cannot tunnel underground or hide themselves in other such ways. Also, more people have studied birds than any other group of animals. Nevertheless, there are many species, genera or families the relationships of which are obscured by anatomical or other peculiarities and which have long been a matter of perplexity. A refined technique has now been devised to overcome this, so far as birds are concerned. In this use is made of electrophoresis, an electro-chemical method for the fragmentation of mixtures of charged particles. A sample of fresh egg-white is applied to a strip of filter paper saturated with a suitable buffer solution. A constant direct current is applied for a standard period causing the different proteins to move through the filter paper at speeds differing according to the net charge, size, shape and other features. These properties depend primarily on the sequence of amino acids in the protein chain. The pattern of this sequence is inherited. Therefore, the electrophoretic behaviour of the proteins gives a clue to the genetic make-up of the species.

After the current has been applied the protein on the filter paper is dyed and the strip can then be scanned with a photo-electric densitometer. A pen-drawn curve is produced which indicates the position and amounts of the proteins present in the egg-white. The electrophoretic profile so obtained can be compared with those of other species. It amounts almost to finger-printing with great accuracy the species, families and orders of birds.   M.B.

EGGS, the female germ cells, or ova, found in all animals. In everyday speech the term is restricted to those eggs which are deposited by the female and develop outside the body, such as the eggs of birds and reptiles on land or of fishes and amphibians usually in water. The term is misused rather more severely when applied only to the egg-shell – as is frequently so when birds' eggs are referred to – or to later developmental stages as in 'ants' eggs', which are in fact pupae.

The egg is the single cell which, usually only after fertilization by a single sperm cell, develops into the embryo by a complicated process of division, growth and reorganization, It is formed in the female primary sex organ or gonad, the ovary, and in a number

The largest and the smallest eggs of living birds, ostrich and hummingbird.

of groups, particularly the fishes, reptiles and birds, has a food store of yolk enclosed within its outer membrane. Thus the eggs of birds, such as the extinct Elephant birds, Aepyornithidae, with a capacity around two gallons, have been designated the largest animal cells. In the majority of animals the welfare of the eggs is dependent upon the functioning of a variety of accessory organs, whether the egg is shed from the body or not. Thus in animals which deposit their eggs in the external medium there are special glands, chambers or passages in the female the function of which is to add protective or nutritive materials to the egg cell proper and to guide its passage to the outside.

In animals which retain the egg in the body for development a special area of tissue is usually developed, the placenta, through which nutritive materials pass to the growing embryo and excretory materials pass from it. In certain invertebrates, fishes and amphibians the eggs may be retained by one or other of the sexes after being shed from the body and in these cases special accessory structures or behaviour may be developed for the attachment or enclosure of the eggs.

The egg cell is basically like all other cells in that it is composed of cytoplasm and nucleus surrounded by a limiting membrane. However, during the maturation process in the animal egg cell the number of chromosomes in the nucleus is halved (see meiosis) and the mature egg, therefore, has half the number of chromosomes typical for all other cells of that animal. The full number of chromosomes is restored later when the nucleus of the egg cell and the nucleus of the spermatozoon unite – the sperm nucleus also having the halved number of chromosomes. The cytoplasm contains a variable amount of yolk, according to the species, and one of the ways in which animal egg cells may be classified is according to the arrangement of yolk. In many of the flatworms (phylum

Platyhelminthes) for example the yolk is no enclosed in the egg cell. In the echinoderm (e.g. starfish) and mammals it is more or les evenly distributed through the cytoplasm and in others, e.g. arthropods, fishes an birds, it is restricted within a yolk-sac.

All egg cells are enclosed in a vitellin membrane which is the basic, or primar membrane of the cell. Some animals, such a insects, have a secondary, or chorionic membrane which is formed by separate cell in the ovary and which hardens to form th shell. Extra tertiary structures, includin membranes, may be formed in the oviduct o by accessory glands. In birds the albume ('white') egg membranes and the shell of th egg are all tertiary structures, as are th 'mermaids' purses' commonly to be found o beaches, which are the egg-cases of shark and their close relatives.

The number of eggs produced by an particular species of animal is dependen upon many factors, some of which ar poorly understood, but it is clear that there i a direct relationship between the number o eggs produced and the likelihood of a suffici ent number of those eggs producing youn which will survive long enough to offset th parental death rate. In other words each pai of animals must, if the species is to continu have at least two offspring that survive t maturity thus themselves being able to repro duce. Therefore, animals in which th hazards to eggs or young are considerabl produce considerable numbers of eggs an animals with well-developed and successfu parental care produce few eggs. Certai parasitic life-histories, particularly in the in vertebrates, involve an enormous mortalit of eggs and young during the hazardou process of transfer from one host to another Thus the parasitic roundworm (*Ascaris*) pro duces around 65 million eggs a year – mor than 1,500 times its own body weight – i the intestine of pig or man. Another round worm (*Haemonchus*) preferring the sheep' stomach, produces an egg every 10 to 2(

Trout eggs lying on the river bed before being covered with gravel by the female.

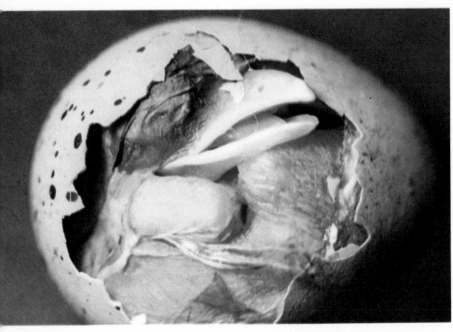

The egg of a bird, in this case the Song thrush *Turdus philomelos*, in the process of hatching.

Slug with its eggs laid in a glass dish in the laboratory.

seconds, while one of the human tapeworms, *Diphyllobothrium latum,* lays several million eggs a day and lives several years. The life-history of this last species explains why such vast numbers of eggs are produced. The tapeworm eggs are passed out in the human faeces and the successful ones will reach water where they hatch into a larvae which, if lucky, find a certain type of water shrimp and enter it. If that shrimp is then eaten by a certain kind of fish another larval stage is developed in the muscles of the fish, and if this is then eaten by man the parasite has been one of the minute proportion of lucky ones. And this is not the most complicated of endoparasitic life-histories.

Other animals which need to produce large numbers of eggs are aquatic animals with external fertilization and embryonic development. Enormous numbers of fishes' eggs and young are lost and the cod may produce 7 million eggs and the ling 50 million. Fishes producing eggs which sink fairly quickly to the bottom produce fewer eggs – the Brook trout up to 6,000 and the herring 30,000.

At the other extreme are the larger birds and mammals which show well-developed parental care and are more independent of the environment. These may not even produce one egg a year, but this is enough to balance mortality, the adults living for several years.

The form of eggs in those animals in which they are 'laid' by the female and not retained in the body varies considerably according to the type of animal and its life-history. And although the eggs of birds are those which, understandably, have most often captured the imagination, the eggs of other groups such as the insects are equally

striking and variable, if on a smaller scale. Lacewings' eggs for example are deposited on stalks, to avoid cannibalism by adjacent larvae, the eggs of butterflies are sculptured in a wide variety of vase-like forms and the Praying mantis deposits its eggs in a cloud of froth which hardens as a protective egg-case. The placing of some parasitic insect eggs is well-nigh incredible; not only does the ovipositing female choose the larva of a particular species of host insect, but she will usually only oviposit on a particular segment of a larva of a particular age.

Extra protective coverings to eggs are not uncommon. The eggs of intestinal parasites may have a coating that is resistant to the

enzymes of the host and there are numerous devices for protection against environmental hazards in those eggs which are deposited in the external medium. The jelly-like coating of frogspawn is well-known. A similar device is also seen in certain molluscs, the eggs being enclosed in jelly in the form of strings or flattened coils, although they may be in protective cases. When eggs are deposited on land they need protection against desiccation and the hard shells of insect and birds' eggs serve this purpose, as do the leathery shells of reptile eggs and the gelatinous coating of the eggs of land slugs and snails.

Highly edible eggs must either be produced in enormous numbers or be concealed

Egg of Royal python *Python regius* in process of hatching. The shell is parchment-like.

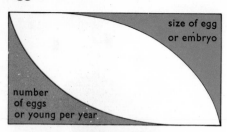

size of egg
or embryo

number
of eggs
or young per year

The size of the eggs (or embryos) bears a fairly strict relation to the numbers produced, although the size of the parent also determines it.

*Numbers of eggs and young
per year.*

1 or less,	some birds and mammals
2–6	many birds and mammals
5–50	reptiles and viviparous fishes
50–300	oviparous fishes with some parental care
5,000	Brook trout
50,000	herring
7,000,000	cod
28,000,000	ling
65,000,000	*Ascaris*
3–400,000,000	tapeworm

in some way from predators. Reptilian eggs are usually hidden in the soil or in litter, but the eggs of many kinds of birds are in full view, at least from above. It is these eggs which show the variety of colouration which has intrigued so many generations of naturalists. Birds' eggs which are concealed in holes tend to be white or pale in colour, but those of species which nest in the open show a great variety of pigmentation which has developed as a cryptic device. Those eggs which are placed on the ground in the open match their background particularly well, as in waders, gulls and terns. The nightjar provides another example, in this case the eggs are deposited on the woodland floor.

The colour pattern of the eggs is much less variable within a species than it is between species, being genetically governed. As the egg passes down the different regions of the oviduct it receives first the albumen, then the two shell membranes, and finally the shell itself which, like the albumen, is deposited in layers. As the layers of shell are laid down pigments are secreted also by the uterus wall and, according to the type and pattern of secretion, so do we see the type

and pattern of shell colouration. Finally a thin cuticle is secreted over the surface of the egg and this also is pigmented, completing the species characteristics of the egg.

The size of birds' eggs relative to the size of the bird varies considerably. The smaller birds produce eggs $\frac{1}{8}$ of their weight or less, while in the larger birds this fraction may be only $\frac{1}{28}$. In the very large flightless birds the fraction is even smaller, but even so the egg of an Elephant bird is equivalent in volume to over 2,000 hummingbird's eggs. There are some striking exceptions to this general size relationship. The kiwi for example lays a relatively enormous egg—about four times as large as would be expected from its size while the cuckoo lays an egg much smaller than one would expect if it were not for the fact that the birds which it parasitizes are much smaller than it is itself.

The mammals care for their fertilized eggs in a very different manner, retaining them inside the female for a period equivalent to the incubation period in birds. Such eggs are relatively simple, but their relationship with the mother is very intimate and complex. See also fertilization.   P.M.D.

EGGS, CLEIDOIC. When an egg is laid on land, as by an insect, reptile or bird, it is surrounded by protective (embryonic) membranes and a shell, and is known as a Cleidoic egg. These outer coverings while allowing some interchange with the surrounding air, such as the passage of oxygen, nevertheless largely isolate the embryo from its surroundings as a self-contained system. It is buffered against the danger of desiccation by its membranes; it feeds on the store of yolk provided in the egg-cell; it breathes by means of a system of embryonic blood-vessels which absorb oxygen through the pores of the shell; it gets rid of its waste products, at least in reptiles and birds, by accumulating them in a sac (developed from the urinary bladder) which is left behind in the broken shell when the embryo hatches. The closed nature of the system has brought about an adaptation which protects the embryo from the danger of intoxication by nitrogenous excretory products such as urea, for this is soluble in water and would be circulated and accumulated in the blood.

Instead, the chemical process of breakdown of nitrogenous products is directed to the production of uric acid, which is insoluble in water. Organisms provided with this type of embryonic metabolism are called uricotelic. Others, such as placental mammals where the excretory products of the foetus are constantly evacuated by the mother and take the form of urea, are called ureotelic. G. de B.

EGG PALATABILITY. With the aid of a tasting panel, Dr H. B. Cott of Cambridge

University investigated the palatability of the eggs of some 200 species of birds. Each egg was scrambled and its taste rated from 10·0 (ideal) to 2·0 (inedible). Eggs of the domestic chicken were rated at 8·7, those of domestic goose and duck at 7·1. The edibility of Blue tit eggs is 4·1, Reed warbler 3·6, wren 2·7 and Black tit 2·0. At the other end of the scale, the eggs of some albatrosses and penguins were given ratings of up to 9·0 although eggs were not available to the panel. R. C. Murphy rhapsodized over the eggs of the Wandering albatross but felt that, at over 1 lb (470 g), they were rather large for one sitting.

The results from the tasting panel supported experiments with egg-eaters such as ferrets and rats showing that an egg's palatability was linked with its vulnerability. Eggs of large birds or of those that nest in inaccessible places are palatable but in those species that nest in vulnerable situations eggs were more palatable if they were camouflaged. Conspicuous eggs, on the other hand, are more readily found by predators and are distasteful. Similarly, Dr Cott found that the flesh of many birds was distasteful if they were brightly plumaged.

EGG-TOOTH, an organ on the snout of hatching embryo reptiles and on the bill of embryo birds used to cut open the eggshell. There are two kinds in reptiles. In turtles, crocodiles and the tuatara it is a small, pointed horny wart formed as a local thickening of the skin on the tip of the snout, and known as the egg caruncle. At hatching, the embryo slits open the flexible membrane lining the inside of the shell, then cracks the calcareous shell itself by stretching movements of the body and limbs. The caruncle is shed within a few weeks of hatching.

The 'egg-tooth' of lizards and snakes is a specialized type of real tooth at the tip of the upper jaw, stouter and longer than a normal tooth. And whereas the other teeth of the upper jaw point towards the lower jaw, the egg-tooth points forwards and outwards. In most species there is only a single egg-tooth, in the midline between right and left jaws. Geckos have a pair of egg-teeth, situated close together at the tip of the jaw, each resembling the typical single egg-tooth of other lizards. In all egg-laying snakes and most lizards the eggs have pliable shells and the embryo apparently slices right through it. After hatching, the egg-tooth (or egg-teeth, in geckos) is discarded, usually within a day or two. In the live-bearing lizards and snakes egg-teeth are reduced to a varying extent, but are usually not completely absent.

The egg-tooth in birds is scale-like and is shed soon after hatching. The American woodcock is exceptional in having a second egg-tooth on the lower mandible, also. Y.L.W.

Little egret male ceremonially handing to the female a stick, used as nesting material, on coming to the nest to take over duties.

EGRET, name given to certain herons, usually those with an all-white plumage. The egrets do not constitute a natural group and the name is applied loosely to many herons of the tribe Ardeini. Thus the Large white (or Great) egret *Egretta alba* is called 'Great white heron' in some parts of its range. It cannot even be said that members of the genus *Egretta* are egrets, for the maritime *Egretta sacra* is almost invariably named Reef heron. Similarly members of the genus *Ardeola* are variously named, the white *Ardeola ibis* is the Cattle egret, while *Ardeola ralliodes,* which is not all-white, is the Squacco heron.

As with other herons, the size and body shape of egrets varies considerably. The Great white egret is the largest. It has very long legs and measures about 3 ft (1 m) in length including the long sinuous neck and daggerlike bill. Among the smaller species is the Little egret *Egretta garzetta* which is only half the size of *E. alba* though with similar proportions. The Cattle egret differs in having a short neck giving it a somewhat hunched appearance. The long legs of the *Egretta* species are an adaptation to wading in shallow water, the long neck must have evolved to meet the need to reach the ground when feeding. The Cattle egret, which normally feeds on dry land, has relatively short legs and therefore a short neck.

Egrets are widely distributed in the tropics and warmer temperate regions of the world. The Great white egret has a particularly extensive range, being found in the warmer parts of five continents. The distribution of the Cattle egret is particularly interesting and gives us a well-documented example of an animal extending its range naturally. Late in the 19th or early in the 20th century, Cattle egrets were found to have colonized part of the northern coast of South America. It is presumed that a party of these birds had crossed the Atlantic from Africa. They in-

Smaller or Lesser egrets *Egretta intermedia*, with, on either side, Openbill storks *Anastomus lamelligerus*.

creased rapidly in their new home and began to spread. The Cattle egret is now abundant and widespread in southeastern North America and in the north of South America and is still spreading. At the other extreme of its range the Cattle egret is moving eastwards into Australia.

Most egrets nest colonially, either in pure colonies or in mixed colonies with other water-birds. In such a mixed colony in East Africa, over 40,000 nests of storks, cormorants, egrets and other herons were counted. These included some 10,000 nests of Cattle egrets, over 1,500 of Little egrets, and smaller numbers of Great white egrets and Yellow-billed egrets *Egretta intermedius* nests. Most egrets build a simple platform of sticks or reeds in trees, or in dense aquatic vegetation. The eggs are usually pale blue or white and both sexes incubate. During the breeding season, male and female egrets become adorned with long white plumes which grow from the nape, back or breast. The plumes are frequently erected and displayed during breeding activities and may function in species recognition. The beautiful white feathers were much sought after a few decades ago, when it was fashionable for ladies to wear ornate headgear.

The diet of egrets varies considerably, a number of them catch fishes and frogs, but some of the smaller species are largely insectivorous. The Cattle egret is named from its habit of gathering in flocks around domestic stock. The birds walk close to the grazing animals, even perching on their backs, and catch the grasshoppers and other insects they disturb. The habit, which is simply an extension of their association with wild buffalo and other big-game animals, has brought them in close contact with man so that they are often extremely tame. FAMILY: Ardeidae, ORDER: Ciconiiformes, CLASS: Aves.   P.W.

EIDER DOWN. Only a few eiderdowns are actually filled with the down used by eiders to line their nests; feathers from domestic birds are a much more usual material. Eider down is, however, still collected on eider farms in Iceland. The female eider lines her nest with down plucked from her breast. This down is collected shortly after the eggs are laid, and the duck replaces this with a second lining which is collected after the eggs have hatched.

Eiders are encouraged to nest on farms by the provision of nest boxes and by protection against predators such as Arctic foxes. The farms are often festooned with coloured streamers and wind-operated musical instruments which it is thought will encourage nesting.

In recent years there has been a sharp decrease in the production of down, which is currently (1969) worth 8/- per nest. At one time there were about 12,500 nests on a farm on the island of Ædey in North West Iceland, but nowadays no colony has more than 6–7,000 nests.

EIDER DUCK, species of arctic sea-duck of the tribe Somateriini. There are four species of Eider duck (placed by some authorities in the tribe Mergini, with the saw-bills), the Common eider *Somateria mollissima*, the

King eider *Somateria spectabilis*, the Spectacled or Fischer's eider *Somateria fischeri* and the Steller's eider *Polysticta stelleri*. The term 'eiders' may refer to any or all of these but the singular 'eider' or 'Eider duck' usually means the Common eider.

Eiders are essentially birds of sea coasts or fresh waters near the sea, feeding by diving from the surface to obtain molluscs crustaceans and other aquatic invertebrates. The Common eider and King eider have a circumpolar distribution while the other species are essentially birds of the arctic coasts of Siberia and Alaska. The Common eider is divided into five distinct geographical races: the European eider *S. m. mollissima* which breeds from Iceland east to Novaya Zemlya; the Pacific eider *S. m. v-nigra* which breeds from northeast Asia eastward to the Canadian North West Territories; the Northern eider *S. m. borealis*, which breed in west Greenland and northeast Canada the American eider *S. m. dresseri*, which breeds principally in Hudson's Bay; and the Faeroe eider *S. m. faeroensis*, breeding only in the islands of that name.

The Common eider is a large, heavily built duck some 23 in (58½ cm) long. The legs are placed rather far back for efficient propulsion in the water and this makes the bird rather clumsy on land. The head has

Male eiders resting peacefully and (below) two males fighting.

Common eland in East Africa. These are the largest antelopes and both male and female have horns.

long, low profile with no distinctive forehead. The male is a very striking bird, basically black beneath and white above, but with black rump and upper-tail coverts and a delicate cream-pink breast. The head has a glossy black crown divided by a central white stripe, with the nape and sides of the neck a distinctive emerald green. The legs and feet vary from yellow to green in the different races and the bill varies from green to orange. In both sexes the pigmented bill covering has a double-horned extension passing up and back over the front of the face towards the eyes. The plumage of the female is a warm brown with a transverse barring of black.

Eiders breed on islands and skerries or on isolated coastlines in tundra and north temperate regions. The nests are usually dispersed but, where suitable nest sites are at a premium, the nests may be close together. The down with which the nests are lined is of very high quality as an insulating medium and has been collected by man for centuries in many parts of the world. In Iceland eiders are protected and encouraged for this purpose and the eider down is a crop of economic importance. Arctic peoples have also long made use of eider skins for clothing and decoration, and this art is not entirely lost at least among the eskimos of Canada.

The young of eiders, in common with other sea-ducklings, leave the nest shortly after hatching and accompany the female to water, in which, after a few hours' experience, they are diving and capturing their own food beneath the surface. FAMILY: Anatidae, ORDER: Anseriformes, CLASS: Aves. P.M.D.

ELAND, the largest of the antelopes, it differs from the kudu and its relatives, in lacking preorbital glands, in the presence of horns in the female, a tufted tail, a pendulous dewlap, a tuft on the forehead of bulls, and in the entirely different spiral form of the horns. It differs from the bongo in the dewlap, forehead tuft and horn form.

A bull eland stands $5\frac{1}{2}$–6 ft (165–180 cm) at the shoulder and weighs $\frac{3}{4}$–1 ton (700–1,000 kg). There is a short mane along the back of the neck. The dewlap is very long and extends all the way from the upper part of the throat to between the forelegs and is tufted for part of its length. The shoulders are slightly hunched, the neck is longer than that of an ox and the head is held higher than the withers. The general colour is reddish brown to buff, becoming a smoky blue-grey in old bulls. Most races have white stripes on the body. The nose is dark, often with a white chevron between the eyes and bulls have a dark thick mat of hair on the forehead.

The Common eland *Taurotragus oryx* of East and South Africa has pointed ears. The horns are comparatively short, with two spiral twists near the base which are so close that they overlap. The southern race, *T. o. oryx,* is duller in colour, without stripes and occurs as far north as the Zambesi. Stripes are, however, indicated in the calves. North of the Zambesi, as well as in parts of Rhodesia, occurs the striped form, *T. o. livingstonii,* which is richer rufous in colour with clear white stripes and a black 'garter' on the inner side of the carpus.

The Giant eland *Taurotragus derbianus* is found from Senegal east to the Nile in Uganda and the Sudan; east of the Nile the Common eland. The Giant eland has longer horns, which are as much as twice the length of the head, a large white spot on each cheek and broad, rounded ears with a dark bar on the inside. The neck is darker than the body, often bordered behind by a white stripe and the dewlap is more extensive, beginning just behind the chin. This species, too, is divided into two subspecies: Lord Derby's eland *T. d. derbianus,* found from Senegal to Togo, which is deep chestnut with a black neck, always bordered behind by a white stripe in front of the shoulder, a chocolate-coloured forehead tuft, dark sides to the head and massive divergent horns; and the Sudan

Giant eland *T. d. gigas,* found from south of the Benue River to the Nile. The latter is lighter in colour (pale fawn), with a grey neck and usually no white 'collar', a blackish frontal tuft, grey or fawn sides to the head and straighter, less divergent horns. Both are clearly striped. Lord Derby's eland is an extraordinarily beautiful animal, its dark rufous and black colouration contrasting well with the white stripes, nose-stripe and cheek-spots. It is almost extinct, being represented perhaps by a few dozen animals in two isolated areas: western Togo and eastern Ghana, and the Gambia-Senegal-Guinea-Mali border area.

Elands inhabit open forests and bush country, where they browse, breaking down high branches with their horns. They live in herds of 12–30, but sometimes gather into groups of 100 or more. Each herd has one or two bulls, but many bulls are solitary. The herd is continuously on the move, restlessly, moving at a fast walk, its members snatching food as they go and walking in single file. They are usually quite silent as they move, but occasionally a bull makes a low grunt to signal to the rest of the herd and calves bleat to their mothers. During the dry season elands will dig up bulbs with their hoofs and eat melons, and at this time the big migrating masses are formed. When alarmed, they pause, then gallop away excitedly, often leaping over each other's backs. They have been known to clear obstacles at least 6 ft (2 m) high. They are placid, and rarely defend themselves.

Elands, at least the females, become sexually mature at two years. The female's cycle lasts three weeks, during which she is on heat for three or four days. Gestation lasts nine months and calves are born at different seasons in different parts of Africa: from August–October in Rhodesia, June–August in Zambia and at two periods (March–May and August–September) in the Kruger National Park. The average life-span is 14–16 years, but one cow has been recorded as living 23 years.

There are 6,500–9,500 elands on the Serengeti plains, and there are also large concentrations elsewhere. Ever since Lord Derby's eland beef dinner more than 100 years ago, the domestication of this highly productive antelope has been 'imminent'. Now at last it has happened: at Mbarara Stock Farm in Uganda, at Zezani in Rhodesia, and in Askania Nova Zoological Park in the Ukraine, where four bulls and four cows were imported in 1892. More than 400 eland have been bred here and there is at present a milking herd of 27. Lactation lasts generally for 220–250 days, and each eland gives up to $1\frac{1}{2}$ gal (7 lt) of milk per day. The milk has 11–12 per cent fat and 6–10 per cent protein, that is, about twice as much as is contained in a domestic cow's milk. The milk has one and a half to three times as much calcium and phosphorus. It has less vitamin B_1 and B_2, but more B_3 and biotin, and the same amount of B_{12}. It keeps longer and reduces the acidity of gastric juice, thus benefitting sufferers from gastric and duodenal ulcers. The milk is reportedly delicious—like melted ice-cream.

Beef production has not yet begun, but there is every probability that in this respect, too, the eland will come to rank high among economically beneficial animals. FAMILY: Bovidae, ORDER: Artiodactyla, CLASS: Mammalia.   C.P.G.

ELAPIDS, snakes belonging to the family Elapidae, one of two families of front-fanged snakes, the other being the Hydrophidae or Sea snakes. All are venomous. The family is most strongly represented in Australia. In Asia and Africa they account for only 10% of all snakes, there are only four in North America and none in Madagascar or Europe. Elapids include cobras, King cobra, Coral snakes, kraits, mambas, the taipan and bandy-bandy of Australia and Tiger snakes, all of which are dealt with under these names.

Elapids range from very large snakes, such as the King cobra, almost 20 ft (6 m) long to small Australian snakes less than 15 in (38 cm) long. The bite of the smallest elapids is little worse than a wasp sting. Some of the smaller snakes are sand-coloured but the large members of the family include the brilliant green of the mamba and the striking Coral snakes ringed in black, yellow and red.

The fangs of elapid snakes may be deeply grooved, for conducting venom, or in species such as cobras the edges of the grooves meet to form canals through which the venom flows. Apart from having venom-conducting fangs in the front of the mouth, a condition known as proteroglyphous, there is little to distinguish this family from other poisonous snakes. There is no easily seen external character or combination of characters to serve as a guide and recognition of these dangerous snakes depends on identifying the individual species. FAMILY: Elapidae, ORDER: Squamata, CLASS: Reptilia.

ELECTRIC FISHES occur in several groups of quite unrelated fishes which have independently evolved the ability to discharge an electric current. The two principal uses to which this is put are to incapacitate other creatures (for defence or feeding purposes) or to receive information about the environ-

Elapids are a family of snakes. One of the species is the Green mamba, which although arboreal and only occasionally coming to the ground, can sometimes be seen in water.

Undersea photograph of the Black electric ray of the Mediterranean.

fish thus surrounds itself with an electromagnetic field and any electrical conductor that enters the field will bring a response. In this way, fishes living in muddy waters can detect the presence of prey or of predators. The Elephant-snout fishes are remarkable for the relatively enormous size of their brains, the brain weight equalling $\frac{1}{52}-\frac{1}{82}$ of the total body weight. Since the largest part of the brain in these fishes is the cerebellum and the areas of the hind brain associated with the hearing and lateral line systems, it seems possible that the large brain has evolved in conjunction with the electric organs to process information received from the 'radar system'.

Electric organs in four bony fishes (from top to bottom: Electric eel, Elephant snout fish, African knifefish, South American knifefish) showing their arrangement along the flanks. The lines of force produced by the African knifefish *Gymnarchus niloticus* resemble those of a bar magnet (lower part of diagram). Interference in the field of force can be detected by the fish and interpreted to give information on its surroundings.

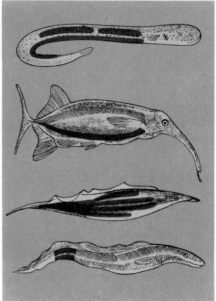

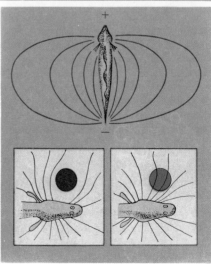

ent in the manner of radar. At first sight, the ability of an animal to generate electricity seems strange. In fact, it is merely an extension of the normal operation of muscles and nerves. Every time an impulse passes down a nerve to stimulate the contraction of a muscle a tiny electric current is involved. In the electric fishes some of the muscles have lost their power to contract but have increased their electrical power. The size and number of nerve endings, where the electricity is normally released, are increased while the electrical units are arranged to multiply the discharge from unit to unit so that a battery effect is achieved. The electrical discharge does not affect the fish itself, largely because of the great insulation round the nerves. The discharge of the organ is controlled by the brain.

Amongst the cartilaginous fishes, the best known species are the Electric rays (*Torpedo* spp). These are Mediterranean and subtropical Atlantic fishes with a round, disc-shaped body and short tail, found over sandy or muddy bottoms. The largest is the Black electric ray *Torpedo nobiliana,* which may reach 5 ft (1·5 m) and weigh 100 lb (45 kg). The electric organs are in the wing-like pectoral fins. They can produce a current of 200 volts, quite enough to stun small crustaceans and fishes on which they feed. Species of the related genus *Narcine* are found in Australia.

The best known of the bony fishes is the Electric eel *Electrophorus* found in the Amazon basin. It is not a true eel, in spite of its eel-like appearance, but is related to the carps and characins. This fish can grow to more than 6 ft (1·8 m). The body is elongated but about $\frac{7}{8}$ of the total length is tail, the alimentary canal, heart, liver, kidneys and gonads being crowded into the first $\frac{1}{8}$. The 'tail' part is largely occupied by the electric organs. These fishes are able to emit two kinds of discharge, a high voltage (over 500 volts) for stunning prey and a much weaker regular pulse used as a direction finder and indicator for locating objects in the vicinity.

The Electric catfish *Malapterurus electricus* is a rather repulsive looking fish found in the Nile system, the Zambesi and certain of the African lakes. It has the Arabic name of *raad* which means 'thunder'. The electric organs are in the muscles over much of the body. These fishes grow to about 4 ft (120 cm) in length and can discharge 350 volts.

The electric organs found in the mormyrids or Elephant-snout fishes are located in the caudal peduncle, the muscular base to the tail. In these fishes a continuous stream of electrical impulses is discharged from the organ, at a variable frequency (lowest when the fish is resting but rising to 80–100 impulses per minute if the fish is disturbed). The

The Knife fish *Gymnarchus niloticus,* related to the Elephant-snout fishes, is shaped rather like a compressed eel and also uses its electric organs for detection of prey and predators. It has rather poor sight and lives in muddy waters.

There is only one group of marine electric bony fishes and this is the stargazers. Members of the genera *Astroscopus* and *Uranoscopus* are bottom-living fishes in which the electric organs are located in deep pits behind the eyes. These organs generate currents of up to 50 volts and this may be used both for defence and for stunning prey.

ELECTRIC ORGANS, known only in certain species of fishes, produce electric discharges which are used by some fishes to stun prey and by others to produce an electric field which is used in orientation.

Weak electric organs are found in two families of freshwater fishes; the gymnotids, or Knife fishes, of South and Central America, and the mormyrids of Africa. An exception is the Electric eel *Electrophorus electricus,* of South America which is a gymnotid that can produce discharges of 550 volts, sufficient to severely shock a man and giving enough current to light an electric light bulb. The only other freshwater fish with strong electric organs is the Electric catfish *Malapterurus,* which can discharge up to 350 volts. Fairly powerful electric organs are also found in the rays and skates (although they are weak in the Thornback ray *Raja clavata*) and in some species of stargazers (*Astroscopus* spp). These species are all bottom-living forms.

The mormyrids are common in the turbid waters of West African rivers, where they were collected by Professor Lissmann in 1951. He observed that one species, *Gymnarchus niloticus,* could swim equally well backwards or forwards, would enter crevices tail first, and could locate prey at surprising distances. *Gymnarchus,* in common with nearly all mormyrids, gymnotids and rays, has spindle-shaped electric organs which replace certain muscles in the tail region. The voltage of the pulse from *Gymnarchus* is usually only a few volts which would have little effect on potential prey, and furthermore, the discharge is a series of pulses produced at a rate of 300 per second, continuing for long periods. Preliminary experiments showed that *Gymnarchus* backed away from metal objects placed in the water and that it could be 'pulled along' by a magnet moved behind a screen outside the aquarium.

Lissmann went on to show, in an elegant series of experiments, that the fishes were sensitive to objects of different conductivity in the water. He trained them to take food from behind porous pots. In one of the first experiments fishes were allowed to take food

from behind a pot containing aquarium water, but were threatened with a wire fork when they attempted to take food from behind a pot filled with paraffin wax. After only a few trials the fishes clearly discriminated between the two pots irrespective of their position in the tank. Similar experiments showed that they could discriminate between distilled water and aquarium water and that they could detect a glass tube 2 mm in diameter at a distance of a few centimetres.

During the discharge, the head of *Gymnarchus* becomes positive with respect to the tail and an electric field is set up around the animal. Objects with a different conductivity from water distort the electric field and the distortions are detected by electroreceptors in the fish's skin. The electroreceptors are numerous jelly-filled pits in the skin which open into flask-shaped invaginations; they are widely distributed over the body surface of the fish.

Electric organs are composed of many stacked elements called electroplates, which are modified from muscle cells, sometimes from the nerve endings (end-plates) on the muscle cells, or (in the Electric catfish) from skin glands. Each electroplate is embedded in jelly-like material and surrounded by connective tissue and, for any particular species, all the electroplates face in the same direc-

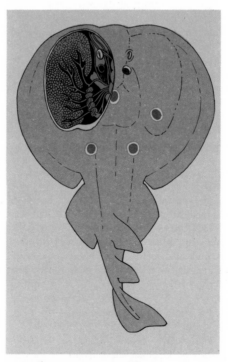

The Electric ray *Torpedo* dissected to show one of the major electric organs with the associated nerve supply. The prismatic areas on the surface of the organ represent the vertical columns of electric plates, of which there may be 500,000 in each organ.

tion. The organ of the Electric eel runs near the whole length of the body and is divided into three parts on each side. Altogether there are about 6,000 electroplates, each of which can generate about $\frac{1}{10}$ volt.

Fresh water has a higher resistance than salt water, and to overcome this most of the electroplates of the Electric eel are connected in series, but 70 of them are connected in parallel, which allows a current flow of about one amp. Among the marine fishes, the Electric ray *Torpedo marmorata* (which was known to the Greeks and used by them for therapeutic purposes) has over 1,000 of its electroplates in parallel and only 400 in series, thereby producing a voltage that is lower (45 volts) but sufficient to overcome the resistance of sea water.

Electric organs typically discharge a series of pulses, which are produced at a rapid rate and over long periods by weakly electrical fishes, but usually only a brief train of pulses is produced by strongly electrical fishes. The long electric organ of the Electric eel is stimulated to discharge by branches of the spinal nerves which run all the way along the body. An intriguing feature is that the discharge of the whole organ is completed in about 1·5 milliseconds after the discharge of the first electroplate, even though conduction in nerves the length of the spinal cord would normally take about 10 milliseconds. The synchronization is achieved mainly by built-in delays in activity of the nerves where they leave the spinal cord and by a gradual shortening of the nerves from the head end towards the tail.

There are indications that some strongly electrical fishes can also use their electricity in orientation, like the gymnotids and mormyrids. The Electric catfish reacts to magnetic fields and becomes highly sensitive to earth currents that are set up some hours *before* earthquakes. The Electric eel can produce trains of weak electric discharges from the part of its electric organ in the tail region, and it also resembles the weakly electrical gymnotids and mormyrids in keeping its body axis in a straight line when it swims (tail movements would disturb an electric field) and like them lives in muddy water.

How electric organs have evolved is a question that has worried many people, including Darwin, but Lissmann has suggested that there may have been three steps in the process. When a fish moves, electrical events in the muscles can be recorded in the water near to the fish, and it is possible that some fishes evolved special receptors which could detect these in conditions in which the use of other senses was difficult. The way was then open for the evolution of weak electric organs which could be used in orientation, and finally, by elaboration of these, strong electric organs, capable of stunning or killing prey could have been evolved.   P.E.H.

African elephants at a water-hole. The long trunk, an elongated nose, enables the elephant to drink without kneeling.

ELECTRO-THERAPY. Before the nature of electricity was understood the ability of certain fishes to cause one's skin to tingle or even one's limbs to jerk was well known in Mediterranean countries and in parts of Africa. As electric fishes were regularly caught for market, fishermen frequently suffered from shocks received when handling them. The Romans thought that the Electric ray released some poisonous substance which congealed the blood and they used live rays to cure gout and headaches, placing the fish against the affected part. Arabs used the electric catfish for similar purposes but the strangest use is that of the brains of Electric rays being used to remove superfluous hair.

ELEPHANT, the largest land mammal, two species of which are known; the African and the Indian. The African elephant *Loxodonta africana,* found only on that continent, has two subspecies, the Bush elephant (subspecies *africana*) and the Forest elephant (subspecies *cyclotis*), the former being larger, more abundant and better known. The Bush elephant is the largest of the elephants, the female reaching an average mature height of 8 ft 4 in (2·5 m) and the males, owing to a post-pubertal growth spurt, 10 ft 2 in (3·1 m). Forest elephants are about 2 ft (0·6 m) smaller and the difference between the sexes is less pronounced. The body weight of an average mature female Bush elephant is 5,900–7,700 lb (2,700–3,500 kg) and the male 10,000–11,700 lb (4,500–5,300 kg). There is a large seasonal variation as well as a variation in weight between populations according to the state of the habitat. The overall length of a large male (trunk to tail) is up to 27 ft (9 m).

In order to support this weight, the limbs are massive columns and are so constructed that the elephant cannot run or jump. The limb bones are heavy and have no marrow and the soles of the feet cover a fatty cushion, which helps to distribute the load evenly. They usually have five and four toe nails on fore- and hindfeet respectively, but they are reduced to three on all feet in some individuals. The ears are large, shaped like a map of Africa and measuring up to 3 ft × 5 ft (1 × 1½ m). They are important in thermo-regulation and in aggressive behavioural displays. The ears of the Forest elephant and the Indian elephant *Elephas maximus* are very much smaller, no doubt related to their more shady habitat. The skull is huge, being modified to support the tusks, which are rooted in large sheaths formed from the premaxillary bones. The brain case is massive, with walls which are thick, but cellular in structure, to give strength with lightness.

The tusks first appear at two to three years of age. They are upper incisor teeth, composed of dentine with a very small, 2 in (5 cm), enamel cap that is quickly worn away. Their shape follows an equable spiral and they continue to grow in length at the rate of 3½–4½ in (9–11·5 cm) a year throughout life, but owing to breakage and wear they only reach about half their potential length. The average lengths of the tusks of the oldest males and females are about 8 ft (2·5 m) and 5 ft (1·6 m) respectively. Their rate of growth in weight increases progressively with age and male tusks are much more massive than female tusks, reaching an average paired weight of 240 lb (109 kg) as compared with 39 lb (18 kg) in females. The world record single tusk weight (from East Africa) is 235 lb (107 kg) for males and 56 lb (25 kg) for females. In some populations, for example in Zambia, tuskless elephants are not uncommon.

The other teeth are also unusual. Because of their longevity and continued growth in size throughout life the elephants need a series of teeth, functionally covering their

(Above) Map showing distribution of modern elephants. (To right) Section through the skull of the African elephant showing a tusk and the succession of molars (and surface of a single molar). (Right below) Tip of trunk of (1) African elephant, with double 'lip' and (2) Indian elephant, with single lip; and, below these, section through lower part of an elephant's leg showing bones of foot and one toe, and the elastic pad encasing the foot.

.life-span and increasing in size as the animal grows larger. This is achieved by having a series of six teeth in each side of each jaw (24 in all) which are formed and replace each other in succession throughout life. No more than one (or two) in each series are wholly (or partly) in wear at any one time and they are progressively larger from the first to the sixth. The teeth themselves are unique, being constructed of a series of flat vertical plates of dentine and enamel, held together by a matrix of cementum. The average number of these plates or laminae increases from three in the first tooth to 13 in the sixth.

The grinding area of the teeth in use in each jaw in a nine-month old calf is only 1·5 sq in (9·4 cm^2) and reaches a maximum of 50 sq in (320 cm^2) and 40 sq in (260 cm^2) in males and females respectively in their late forties. Subsequently, as no more teeth are produced wear results in a reduction of the grinding area to 16 sq in (100 cm^2), they are unable to feed efficiently and death due to 'mechanical senescence' occurs. This sets a limit to the elephant life-span of 60–70 years. The replacement and wear of the teeth can be used as criteria for estimating the age of elephants with surprising accuracy.

The trunk is a huge mobile organ, which has developed as the body size increased during the course of evolution. It has evolved by elongation of the nose and enables the elephant to drink and feed at ground level without kneeling, or developing a long neck

as the giraffe has done. Leaves and branches or creepers up to 20 ft (6 m) above the ground can be picked. The trunk is a very precise manipulative organ, almost a hand in fact, with two mobile finger-like processes and it can select herbs or small tree seedlings among the grass. When drinking, water is sucked up into the hollow trunk and then squirted into the mouth. An anatomical peculiarity of the lungs, which adhere to the pleura, instead of being free within the thorax as in other mammals, may be related to this sucking function. The trunk can be used to excavate deep 'wells' in the bed of seasonally dry rivers, which also benefit other game. It is also used as a directional scent organ.

The elephant has several other peculiarities. The heart has a double apex, giving rise to the misconception that it is a double heart. The breasts are pectoral and there are two nipples behind the front legs at which the young suckle with their mouth (not their trunk). They are non-ruminants and have a relatively small simple stomach and vast large intestine where fermentation occurs. The so-called 'tummy-rumbles', a growling roar characteristic of undisturbed elephants are now known to be produced in the larynx and in fact represent a very loud 'purring'. When elephants are disturbed these sounds cease. The testes of the male are abdominal since, as in the distantly related hyrax, they are not in a scrotum. They have a large slow growing brain which is relatively small at

birth, as in man (35% of mature weight a compared with 26% of mature weight i man). This fact together with a long perio of childhood, stable social organization an relatively great longevity for a mammal important in relation to learning and intell gence. Their life tables are very similar t those of early man with high mortality i calves and a senescent rise in mortality star ing after the age of 47 years or so. There are sex differences in survival, in favour of the female. In one natural population the expectation of further life at an age of 12 months was 21 years in the female and 18 in the male. Like man, the elephant appears to suffer from age-linked diseases, the most noteworthy being arteriosclerosis, or arterial disease.

The senses of sight and hearing are only moderately developed in contrast to the sense of smell which is acute. Smell plays an important part in their social contacts and the trunk is used to locate scents precisely. An unusual organ is the temporal gland, in structure like a modified and vastly enlarged sweat gland, located under the skin between eye and ear on each side of the head. There is a marked sex difference in the size of this gland, which is first apparent in sexually mature, but not yet sociologically mature, males. It seems clear that this is a scent gland used to mark trails or territories. Its duct often contains short twigs acquired as the elephant rubs its head against a tree or bush. There is no indication of 'musth' in the African elephant, a phenomenon associated with this gland in the Indian elephant.

The elephant is one of the few animals that continue to grow throughout life. At birth the Bush elephant calf weighs on average 264 lb (120 kg). Males and females grow at similar rates, the male slightly faster, until about 20 years, when there is an acceleration in the male growth rate in size and weight that results in the great difference between the sexes as adults. This is paralleled by the

growth curves of certain harem breeding seals and whales and suggests that in the elephant bull herds there is a hierarchical organization, the larger bulls being dominant and fathering more calves. However, this 'sociological maturity' is reached on average at an age of 26 years—long after the attainment of sexual maturity.

The average age at sexual maturity varies between the populations that have been studied from 11–20 years, individuals ranging from 7–30 years. The early maturing populations also show more rapid early bodily growth and better physical condition (larger fat reserves and greater body weight relative to height). This is also related to population density and to the condition of the environment, in particular the progress of the change from woodland or bush towards grassland. The female elephant is one of the few wild animals which shows a significant decline in fertility with age. Advancement of this epoch is related to habitat changes in a similar way to that of deferred puberty, the 'menopause' occurring earlier in the populations showing the greatest deferment of maturity.

For females in average stable or increasing populations the interval between births averages about four years, but in populations which have begun to adjust to habitat changes this may lengthen to as much as eight or nine years. The minimum individual recorded calving interval for wild elephants is two and three quarter years, the maximum has been estimated at 13 years. Thus, on the evidence from the incidence of placental

The African elephant with its large ears.

scars in the uterus (marking the sites of previous pregnancies) some females are known to have been pregnant at least eleven times in 40–50 years. Elephants thus demonstrate a remarkable flexibility of response to habitat change involving restriction of the reproductive age groups and a reduction of the level of fertility within them.

There is a definite seasonality in the breeding. Conceptions show a seasonal pattern related to the rainfall cycle and therefore to vegetation quality and production. In western Uganda there is a single breeding season which under natural conditions is related to the first half of the single long wet season. In the drier parts of East Africa there are two conception periods directly related to the two short wet seasons. Farther south, where there is a single moderately short wet season the elephants experience a single conception season. This is presumably adaptive, having evolved so that the calf (which is born 22 months later) has the best chance of survival. The calf is suckled by its mother for at least four years but this is extended to six years or more in populations with low reproductive rates. The fat content of the milk increases with the age of the calf, at least over the first half of the lactation period.

Elephant populations are organized at a number of levels. The basic social unit is the family unit, averaging about six animals and containing an old female, her youngest mature daughter and their surviving immature offspring. Bulls leave the family unit when they reach maturity. About half the mature bulls are solitary and the remainder collect in bull herds usually containing 2–15 animals but occasionally over 100. Single bulls and bull herds form temporary associations with family units and the family units may aggregate to form bigger herds, either an 'extended family' of up to 20–30 fairly

Indian elephant with its young bathing, a favourite and necessary routine for all elephants. It is distinguished from the African elephant by its much smaller ears.

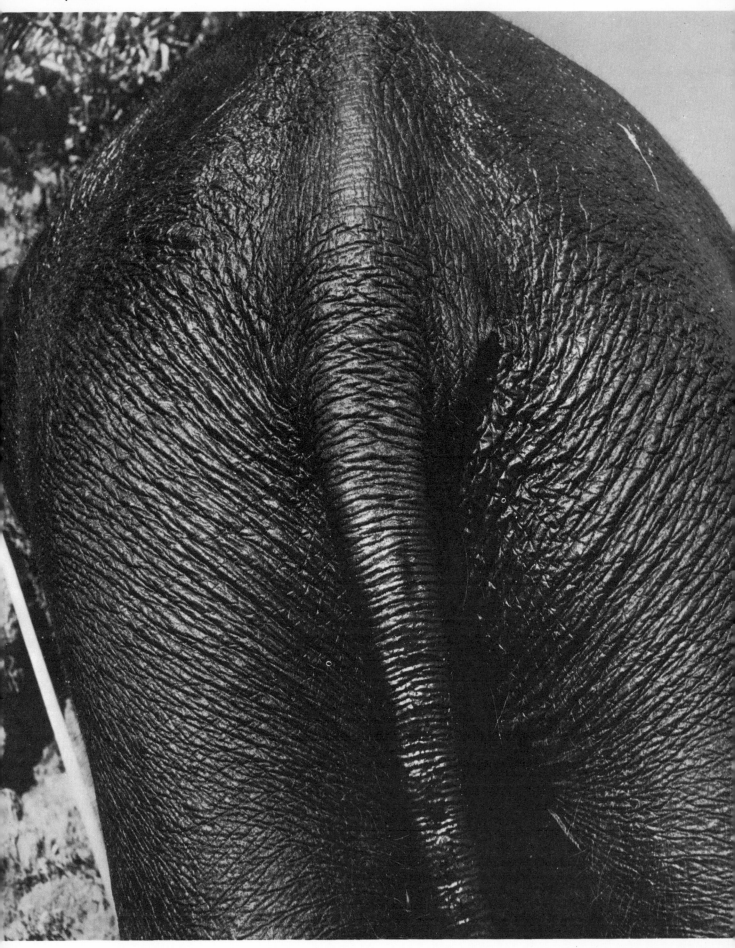

osely related animals, which frequently re-
mbine, or chance aggregations of up to
0 or more. Close ties exist between mem-
ers of family units and examples of eleph-
ts supporting and assisting wounded com-
nions are known. Large herds of as many
1,000 elephants are found in certain situa-
ons, usually at the periphery of populations
at have been displaced by human settle-
ent or activity, or are otherwise in conflict
ith man. These often form spectacular
ght-packed cohorts, leaving a trail of des-
uction in their wake.

As densities increase, average group sizes
rogressively increase, so that a twofold
crease in density leads to a fourfold in-
ease in group size. This in turn leads to a
ore than proportional increase in the in-
nsity of feeding activity and impact on the
abitat.

The daily cycle is one of fairly continuous
ovement in search of food or water, and
rger groups tend to be more mobile. In
vannah regions the hot hours of the middle
the day are often spent resting in the
ade—and the destruction of shade by the
ephants' own activity may lead to an in-
ease in the mortality rate, especially of
oung calves, from heat stress. Elephants eat
od equivalent to about 4% of their body
eight daily and cows with suckling calves
bout 6%. For a large bull this amounts to
me 600 lb (270 kg). The preferred diet
ontains only about 30–50% grass, the
eater amount being taken in the wet
ason. The remainder of the diet comprises
rowse, herbs, bark, fruits and roots. In
xtreme conditions, following the destruction
woody growth, grass comes to constitute
0–90% of the food taken. The elephants
en experience a deficiency of certain
utrients which in turn probably leads to
educed growth rates, deferred puberty, ad-
ancement of 'menopause' and general
owering of fertility. Malnutrition may well
ontribute to increased mortality among
oung calves. It is likely that the pushing
ver or barking of trees at the beginning of
e rains is related to the need to supplement
e low fibre content of young, growing
rass.

The process of habitat change initiated by
lephants involves first the destruction of the
nderstory of bush and tree regeneration,
hich opens the canopy and the less shady
onditions then allow grass to penetrate the
oodland or forest. This in turn provides fuel
or grass fires and the de-barking of mature
rees renders them more susceptible to the
ffect of fires. However, in nearly all cases
hat have been studied the effect of fire on
his process is secondary to the effect of

African elephant picking fruit, and demonstrating one of the many uses to which the trunk can be put.

eft: the preferred view of an angry elephant.

ight: African elephants playing in Lake Edward.
athing sessions are both health-giving and an
pportunity for elephantine fun.

elephant damage. In the past there has been a dynamic succession (its exact nature related to the climate), from bush, woodland, or forest to open moist grassland or dry or semi-desert grassland, and back to the former wooded condition. Increasing human populations prevent elephant populations from dispersing to more wooded areas when the change to grassland becomes limiting, and the cycle is trapped in the grassland phase. This is becoming a serious conservation problem in many areas.

The elephant is a relatively recent arrival in East and South Africa, having dispersed from the West African forest region in the Upper Pleistocene, at a time of higher rainfall when there was an extension of forest areas enabling elephants to cross former barriers created by extensive tracts of grassland (which is not a suitable habitat for them). The Bush elephant then probably split off from the Forest elephant and colonized more open woodland and bushed areas where their food was more abundant than in the forest. This probably led to the development of larger populations and higher densities. It also involved adaptive changes in morphology, physiology and behaviour related to the new environment. The Forest elephant is now confined to the Congo forests and West Africa and there is a zone of interbreeding and hybridization where its range meets that of the Bush elephant, for example in western Uganda. A small Pigmy elephant *Loxodonta pumilio* has been proposed as a distinct species, but it seems more likely that this is a small race of the Forest elephant.

Elephants were formerly abundant throughout Africa and rock paintings in the Sahara even attest to their former presence there. African elephants from near there were used by Hannibal. They are now absent from North Africa, the Sahara and from most of South Africa. Elsewhere their distribution has become more and more discontinuous in competition with the expanding human population.

There is much less information on the biology of the Indian elephant *Elephas maximus*. It differs from the African elephant in its shape (arched back and domed head), smaller tusks, often absent in the female, and much smaller ears. The end of the trunk has only a single process as campared with the two 'fingers' of the African genus. In general it appears to be an animal of jungle or bush country, although it is found in grassland areas. Another point of interest is that, in contrast to the African elephant there is a progressive loss of pigment with age, from the trunk and ears, which consequently develop pale patches. Albinos are also probably more frequent. 'Musth' is a condition peculiar to the Indian elephant which is seldom observed in fe-

males. It is associated with wild aggressive behaviour and copious secretion from the temporal gland. The phenomenon of 'musth', may be enhanced in captivity but the Indian elephant does appear to be quite different from the African elephant in this respect.

This species is now found in India, Assam, Burma, Siam, Malaya, Sumatra and Ceylon, with a few also in Borneo. They seem to frequent as wide a range of habitats as the African species.

The longevity and social organization appear to be similar, but populations and group sizes are in general much smaller than in the African Bush elephant. The newborn calf weighs about 200 lb (90 kg), adult shoulder height is from 8–10 ft (2·5–3 m) and weight up to 10,000 lb (4,500 kg). There is no evidence for a post-pubertal growth spurt in the male and the difference in size of the sexes is much less than in the Bush elephant. Ceylon elephants are much larger than Burma elephants. Sexual maturity is attained between about 8 and 14 years, but there are probably habitat-dependent changes as in the African species.

Little is known of the Indian elephant's behaviour in the wild although there is an extensive lore and mythology associated with working elephants and ceremonial elephants. They are still captured in the course of a special hunt—the Keddah—and trained for moving teak, logs and other work. Most military elephants in antiquity were Indian elephants and some Indian princes had elephant cavalry numbering several hundred. Hannibal's elephants were, however, African elephants. Circus elephants are invariably Indian. FAMILY: Elephantidae, ORDER: Proboscidea, CLASS: Mammalia.   R.M.L.

ELEPHANT, ORIGINAL JUMBO. The first live African elephant to be exhibited in England became famous on both sides of the Atlantic and its name, Jumbo, became a pet-name for any elephant. Jumbo arrived at London Zoo in 1865 and soon became a favourite, giving rides and accepting buns. In later years he became increasingly bad-tempered and while his fate was being debated, a request to purchase him was received from P. T. Barnum, the American showman. The offer was accepted but it brought howls of protest from the public and an injunction was taken out to prevent his export. Eventually, Jumbo's voyage across the Atlantic was effected, after a near accident when he tweaked with his trunk the tail of one of the horses drawing his cage and caused the team to bolt. Jumbo was as well received in America as in England but in 1885 he was fatally injured by a railway train. His body is now to be seen in the American Museum of Natural History, New York.

ELEPHANT BIRD, name given to variou extinct giant flightless birds of which a con siderable amount of fossil and sub-foss material has been discovered in Madagasca There are indications from bone and eggshe fragments that these birds were at one tim more widespread in Africa and tha Madagascar was, therefore, their last strong hold. The Madagascar remains are of recer enough origin to make it likely that the giants finally became extinct in historic time, and it may be that the birds, their eg or their recent remains gave rise to th legend of the roc.

A number of different species of Elephan birds probably lived in Madagascar an these have been grouped into the gener *Aepyornis* and *Mullerornis* in the fami Aepyornithidae. By virtue of certain skelet characteristics they are usually placed wit the large living flightless birds, such as th ostrich and the recently-extinct moas, in th general assemblage of *'ratites'*.

All the Elephant birds that we know c were large, heavy birds with very stron skeletons, somewhat like a very bulk ostrich. The largest was *Aepyornis titan*, 1 ft (3 m) or more in height and with correspondingly strong skeleton. Th species probably weighed 1,000 lb (450 k or more. From time to time Elephant bird eggs are washed out of the soil or sandy lak beaches in Madagascar and are, appropri ately, seen to be enormous. The largest more than 1 ft (30 cm) long and must hav had a capacity of around 2 gal (9 litres) an been equivalent to seven ostrichs' eggs c 12,000 hummingbirds' eggs. Some of th eggs found still contain the bones c embryos. Elephant birds' eggs have bee described as the largest animal cells, but must be remembered that the bird's eg contains a considerable amount of food stor external to the egg-cell proper.

As with other flightless birds such as th dodo, the Great auk, and the moas, Elephar birds were able to survive in their islan stronghold because of the absence of larg effective predators. When man appearec with his destructive behaviour and destruc tive animals, the flightless birds wer doomed. FAMILY: Aepyornithidae, ORDER Aepyornithiformes, CLASS: Aves.   P.M.E

ELEPHANTIASIS, disfiguring disease o man caused by a parasitic filariid roundworm belonging to the genus *Wuchereria*. The mos common species *W. bancrofti* is transmittec from one person to another by the bite c blood-sucking mosquitoes (*Culex* or *Ano pheles*) which act as intermediate hosts for th parasite. Infections with *Wuchereria* are restricted to warm, humid regions of the world and occur in coastal Africa and Asia the Pacific and in South America.

The blood of humans infected with the

Southern elephant seals in their rookery on Annenkov Island, South Georgia, in October, the pupping season.

rasite contains the microfilaria stage of the worm, that is the fully developed embryos still within their thin, flexible egg-shells, that have been released from the mature female worms. During the day the microfilariae accumulate in the blood vessels of the lungs, but at night, when the mosquitoes are feeding, the microfilariae appear in the surface blood vessels of the skin and can be taken up by the insects as they suck blood. The daily appearance and disappearance of the microfilariae in the peripheral blood is controlled by the activity pattern of the infected person and is reversed when the person is active at night and asleep during the day. It is an impressive example of the evolution of close interrelationships between parasites and their hosts and ensures maximum opportunity for the parasite to complete its life-cycle. Microfilariae that are taken up by a mosquito undergo a period of development in the body muscles of the insect before becoming infective to man. When the mosquito next feeds, the larvae escape from the proboscis and enter the bite-wound, thus gaining access once more to the body of the human host.

The adult worms may reach a length of 4 in (10 cm), but are very slender. They live in the lymphatic system of the body, often forming tangled masses of worms and their presence may give rise to recurrent fevers and pains. In long-standing infections, however, far more severe effects may be seen, brought about by a combination of allergic reactions to the worms and the effects of mechanical blockage causing accumulation of lymph in the tissues. Certain regions of the body are more commonly affected than others, notably the limbs, breasts, genitals and certain internal organs, which become swollen and enlarged. The skin in these areas becomes thickened and dry and eventually resembles that of an elephant (hence elephantiasis). In severe cases the affected organ may reach an enormous size and thus bring about debilitating or even fatal secondary complications. The length of time necessary for such changes to take place is variable and may depend on the resistance of the host and the number of worms present and many infected hosts may never develop elephantiasis as such. Drug treatment for the elimination of the worms is useful in the early stages of infection, but little can be done where chronic disease has produced true elephantiasis. Indeed, the parasites may no longer be present by that time. Precautions against the transmitting mosquitoes, such as nets, insecticides and drainage of their breeding areas are the most important preventive measures in endemic regions. ORDER: Filarioidea, CLASS: Nematoda, PHYLUM: Aschelminthes.   D.W.

ELEPHANT SEALS, largest of the Earless seals.

There are only two species: the Northern *Mirounga angustirostris,* and the Southern *Mirounga leonina.* The generic name *Mirounga* is believed to come from the Australian aboriginal word for the seal, 'miouroung'; *angustirostris* is Latin for 'a narrow snout', and *leonina* for 'lion-like', referring both to the size of the animal and also to the roaring noise it makes.

The Northern elephant seal occurs on the islands off the coast of southern California and Mexico from San Miguel in the Santa Barbara group in the north to San Benito in the south, but breeds only on San Miguel, San Nicolas, Guadalupe and San Benito. Stray animals may be found much farther afield and have been reported from British Columbia and Alaska. No general migration takes place, but in spring it is found that most of the adult males are missing from the beaches and are presumed to be out at sea.

Breeding colonies of the Southern elephant seal are to be found on the sub-antarctic islands of South Georgia, South Orkneys, South Shetlands, Kerguelen, Heard, Macquarie, Campbell, Falkland, Gough, Marion and Crozet. The largest breeding population is on South Georgia where there are about 310,000 animals.

Elephant seals

Kerguelen and Macquarie also carry large populations, 100,000 and 95,000 respectively. Nonbreeding groups of animals are to be found on Tristan da Cunha, St Paul and Amsterdam Islands, and in the Vestfold Hills in Antarctica. Wandering animals are reported from varying points in Antarctica, and also from South Africa, Australia, New Zealand and Tasmania. The present breeding range of the Southern elephant seal is now expanding to include those places from which it was previously wiped out by commercial exploitation. Elephant seals do not migrate. They are on their breeding grounds in spring for breeding, and in summer for moulting, but during the rest of the year they are feeding widely dispersed out at sea.

In size and general appearance the two Elephant seals are similar. The adult male may be 16–20 ft (4·8–6 m) in nose to tail length and up to about 8,000 lb (3,628 kg) in weight. The adult female is smaller, being 10–12 ft (3–3·6 m) in length and weighing about 2,000 lb (907 kg). The pup at birth is about 4 ft (1·2 m) in length and 80 lb (36 kg) in weight.

The hair of Elephant seals is short and stiff and the general colour is dark grey. Fighting between the bulls leads to much scar tissue about the neck and chest and the skin here gets very rough and thick.

The inflatable snout or proboscis of the adult male is its most characteristic feature. This is an enlargement of the nose and has the normal internasal septum and two nostrils. When fully developed it overhangs the mouth in front so that the nostrils open downwards, and its elongated cushion-like shape is marked by two transverse grooves. It is less obvious out of the breeding season, but during the breeding season it can be erected by inflation, muscular action and blood pressure, and may act as a resonating chamber to increase the volume of a big bull's roar. There is no such enlargement in females, and in males the development of the proboscis starts when the animal is about two years old. Its full size is reached at about eight years old.

Bulls may reach an age of 20 years, but when the population is being used commercially they seldom live more than 12 years. They become sexually mature at four or five years old, but although they are then capable of breeding, they are not strong enough to hold a harem against older bulls, a status they do not normally acquire until they are 7–12 years old.

The breeding season of the Southern elephant seal starts at the beginning of September. The bulls come ashore first, followed by increasing numbers of females from about the middle of the month. By the end of the month there are enough animals present to form harems, each male presiding over a small number of females at first, later in-

Moulting Southern elephant seal on Bird Island, South Georgia, in December.

At the moult the Southern elephant seal sheds sheets of skin with the old hairs embedded in them.

creasing his harem up to 30–40 females. Each harem has one dominant bull whose function is to mate with the females of that harem, and prevent other bulls from doing so. Younger mature bulls hang about the edges of the harem, sometimes managing to steal a female. A challenger to a reigning harem bull may threaten by roaring for some time. The reigning bull may then retreat without a fight or may stand his ground. If this does not deter the challenger a fight will take place, the victor taking the harem.

Most of the pups are born in October and are 4 ft (1·2 m) long and clad in black woolly hair. Their mothers feed them for about 23 days and towards the end of this period each pup will be putting on about 20 lb (9 kg) a day, while the mother, remaining on land without feeding until the pup is weaned, may lose 700 lb (317 kg) during lactation. Elephant seal milk is of the very rich seal

type, containing 40–50% fat (compared wi 9% in a dog and 3·5% in man), and enabl the babies to quickly put on a thick layer blubber as a protection against the cold. about 35 days old the pup sheds its bla coat for a silvery grey one and is rea to enter the sea. The cows mate again abo 18 days after the birth of the pup and, after is weaned, they go off to sea to feed. On the cows have left, the bulls become muc less aggressive and they too, having fast since the beginning of the breeding seaso return to the sea to feed. As is usual wi Pinnipedia, with the probable exception the walrus, after fertilization the developi blastocyst does not become implanted in t uterus wall for about four months. The cau of this delay is not known, and it is n restricted to pinnipeds, but it does mean th with a normal gestation period of seven a a half to eight months the pups are born approximately the same time each year, at a time when all the adults are concentrated together.

After the breeding season, the next gathering of adult animals is for moulting in December, January and February. The moult takes about 30–40 days and again no food is taken during this time. At the moult large sheets of skin are shed with the old hairs embedded, pushed out by the developing new hair, instead of the more normal method of shedding single hairs. This method seems to be common to all phocids, but has been particularly noticed in Elephant seals. The animals assist the moulting process by rubbing themselves against rocks and immersing themselves in muddy wallows.

Elephant seals have few enemies besides man, though Killer whales and Leopard seals may take the young of the Southern elephant seal and Killer whales and sharks the young of the northern species.

Although most of the above description refers particularly to the Southern elephant seal, the life history of the Northern elephant seal is, as far as is known, similar. The pups are born in December and January and the harems are smaller, usually of only about 12 females. The females mate during lactation and go to sea to feed during lactation. The main anatomical difference between the Southern and Northern elephant seals is in the head. In the latter the snout region of the skull is narrower, and the proboscis is very long, hanging down for about 1 ft (0·3 m) below the mouth when at rest. When erected the proboscis curves inside the open mouth so the nostrils are directed down the throat which acts as an additional resonating chamber, and rhythmic metallic notes are produced.

The total population of the Northern elephant seal has been estimated to be about 15,000 animals—which is a good recovery from the ravages of commercial fishermen, who by 1890, after 70 years of taking as many animals as possible, had reduced the species to about 100 animals.

The Southern elephant seal was also severely reduced by sealers who, having exploited the Fur seals, then turned their attentions to the Elephant seal for oil. By the end of the 19th century they had so reduced the numbers that it was no longer profitable to hunt the Elephant seal. Gradually the numbers built up so that the animals again became useful commercially, but this time under controlled conditions. Most sealing took place on South Georgia and the coastline was divided into four sectors which were worked in rotation, one part remaining untouched each year. There was also a close season for the other three between November and February, but in effect the movements of the seals are such that they

were usually only taken in September and October. There was an upper limit, revised annually, to the number of seals that could be taken, and for several years it was set at 6,000. These had to be bulls only, and had to be above 11 ft 6 in (3·5 m) in length. There is, however, no longer any sealing on South Georgia. Elephant seal oil has much the same properties as whale oil, and is used together with vegetable oils in the manufacture of edible fats. FAMILY: Phocidae, ORDER: Pinnipedia, CLASS: Mammalia.

J.E.K.

ELEPHANT SHREWS, a very distinctive family of small mouse- or rat-sized animals confined to Africa. Although usually classified in the order Insectivora, along with the other shrews, the Elephant shrews differ from other insectivores in so many ways that their relationships are very uncertain. Some authors have considered them related to the equally controversial tree-shrews of southeastern Asia; others have placed them in an order of their own, the Macroscelidea. They have a remarkable resemblance, both in structure and way of life, to some of the marsupial mice of Australia although this could be attributed to convergent evolution.

The most distinctive feature of Elephant shrews, as the name indicates, is the long, pointed proboscis, adapted for nosing out ants, termites and other insects, for these constitute the staple diet. Otherwise they have a fairly normal mouse-like build, adapted for running swiftly on the ground. The hindlegs and feet are longer than the front, hence the

alternative name of Jumping shrews. This is, however, a misnomer for they do not jump bipedally like jerboas but run with lightning dashes, using the powerful hindlegs for thrust as in a hare. The eyes are large and bright, adapted to daytime vision, for Elephant shrews are predominantly diurnal. The tail is usually as long as the head and body and almost naked. In one form, however, a subspecies of *Petrodromus tetradactylus*, there is a remarkable row of stiff bristles on the underside of the tail, each bristle ending in a spherical knob. This arrangement is unique amongst mammals and its function is quite unknown.

Most of the 15 or so species of Elephant shrew have rather uniform brown or grey fur on the upper side, usually closely matching the colour of the local soil. Living in open grassland or semi-desert and, being diurnal, they need protection from aerial predators as they forage for food, usually within sprinting distance of shelter in the form of rocks or bushes. One group, however, the large Forest elephant shrews *Rhynchocyon,* are much more boldly patterned in black and rufous, or finely chequered to match the dappled background of the forest by day.

The reproduction of Elephant shrews shows several peculiarities. The litter size is almost always limited to one or two, the young being very large and well developed at birth. Most mammals shed only a small number of eggs from the ovaries at each ovulation. Most Elephant shrews do the same, but some species, very closely similar in every other respect, are remarkable in regularly

Elephant shrew showing the long snout used for nosing out insects.

Elephant shrews in a German zoo. Their alternative name of Jumping shrews is a misnomer.

releasing over 100 eggs at each ovulation in spite of the fact that the uterus is not adapted to allow more than two to develop. The significance of this remains a mystery.

Elephant shrews are found throughout east, central and southern Africa, but one isolated species, *Elephantulus rozeti*, is found in Morocco and Algeria. Other species of *Elephantulus* are found throughout the savannah and sub-desert zones south of the Sahara (except in West Africa where the whole group is curiously absent). The Chequered elephant shrew *Rhynchocyon cirnei* is found in the Congo forest north of the Congo River and in many forest areas of eastern Africa, showing enormous geographical variation in colour and pattern, a situation rare in mammals but found in some other diurnal groups like the squirrels and monkeys.

In captivity Elephant shrews are timid and nervous. They are rather difficult to keep and have very rarely been bred in captivity. FAMILY: Macroscelididae, ORDER: Insectivora, CLASS: Mammalia.   G.B.C.

ELEPHANT-SNOUT FISHES, freshwater African fishes related to the Bony tongues. In some species, such as *Gnathonemus numenius* and *G. curvirostris,* the snout is elongated and turned downwards, much like an elephant's trunk, with the small mouth at the tip. In other species only the soft lower lip is elongated (e.g. *Gnathonemus petersi*) and in yet others the snout is bluntly rounded with no elongation. In spite of this, all the members of the family Mormyridae have a quite unmistakable look, with smoothly scaled bodies, dorsal and anal fins set opposite to one another, the body brownish grey or slaty grey and a rather delicate forked tail on a slender base (caudal peduncle). There are about 100 species found in the lakes and rivers of Africa, mostly feeding on invertebrates at the bottom. Most are small but some reach 5 ft (1·5 m) in length and they vary from the rather squat species of *Petrocephalus* to the long and eel-like *Mormyrops.*

A number of species are found in the Nile and these seem to have fascinated the Ancient Egyptians, who depicted them in tomb drawings, mummified them and produced amulets in the form of mormyrids. In some parts of Africa where mormyrids are no longer found they nevertheless appear in primitive cave paintings.

Relative to body weight, the mormyrids have very large brains, the ratio brain-weight to body-weight being about the same as in man. In aquaria their behaviour suggests a fair degree of intelligence since they will

Gnathonemus elephas, one of the Elephant snout fishes that truly lives up to its name. Most species have a less pronounced 'trunk'.

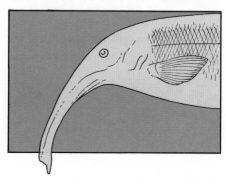

'play' for hours with small objects, leaves etc. reminding one of the 'play' of dolphins. They are also amenable to teaching.

Mormyrids often live in murky waters and their eyesight appears to be poor. In compensation, the muscles at the slender base of the tail are modified into electric organs which can detect obstacles or predators. A small electric field is set up round the fish which acts in the same way as radar (see Electric fishes).

The mormyrids are peaceable fishes in an aquarium and thrive on live foods and on the detritus at the bottom of the tank. In the wild some form shoals when small but become solitary when adult. Some migrate up rivers to spawn but little is known of their breeding habits. FAMILY: Mormyridae, ORDER: Mormyriformes, CLASS: Pisces.

ELFIN SHARK, *Mitsukurina owstoni,* also known as the Goblin shark, a grotesque shark with a long and pointed snout separated from the upper jaw by a deep cleft to give the appearance of a horn. As in the Frilled shark, the tail continues the line of the body and is not bent upwards as in other sharks. There are two dorsal fins and five gill slits. The teeth are awl-shaped but split into two basal lobes, the blade of the tooth becoming shorter at the edges of the jaws. This species was first discovered in deep water off Japan in 1898 and it created considerable interest because members of this family had previously only been known from the fossil genus *Scapanorhynchus* of the Upper Cretaceous rocks. The Elfin shark, which can reach a length of 14 ft (4·2 m), is now known from Indian waters and from Portugal. FAMILY: Scapanorhynchidae, ORDER: Pleurotremata, CLASS: Chondrichthyes.

ELK *Alces alces,* a large European member of the *deer family closely related to the moose of North America and almost identical with it. The name is also used in North America as an alternative to wapiti, the North American equivalent of the Red deer. There was also the Irish elk *Cervus giganteus*, remains of which are found in peat bogs in Ireland and in other Pleistocene deposits in Europe. The Irish elk stood 6 ft (2 m) high, had palmated antlers, similar to those of the Fallow deer but of enormous size, up to 11 ft (3·7 m) across.

ELTON, C. S., British ecologist, born 1900, Director of the Bureau of Animal Populations, Oxford University since 1932.

One of the most important figures in the development of modern ecological thinking, Elton may be regarded as one of the founders of the 'community' approach to ecology. His early experience as a member of several Oxford University Expeditions to the Arctic during the 1920's stimulated his interest in

e population cycles of small herbivorous
mammals. During the 1930's he undertook
detailed study of the mechanisms producing
opulation fluctuations, and concerned him-
elf particularly with the effect of competition
etween different species. At the same time,
lton was developing the idea of the community as a functional system whose consti-
uent populations were related through *food-
hains. By considering plants as well as
nimals, he showed that any food-chain
onsisted of a restricted number of links, and
at the number of individual organisms
ecreased progressively from one end of a
ood-chain to the other. He defined this
henomenon as 'a pyramid of numbers' in
hich the rich abundance of plants formed
e base, the second stage being represented
y the rather fewer herbivorous animals, and
e apex by the very low densities of
arnivorous animals. Subsequent develop-
ents of this idea have led to the definition of
yramids of *biomass and energy as more
ecise ways of interpreting community
tivity, but Elton's functional approach to
e study of communities remains as one of
e major features of present-day ecology.

MBIOPTERA, a small group of insects
und in the warmer regions of the world and
even there not often encountered. They live in
groups of about 20 in silken tunnels built in
bark and particularly over its surface, or
under and between rocks. Here they remain
most of their lives and, if one is exposed by
opening the tunnel, it runs away very fast,
backwards or forwards with equal ease
through the hidden maze. Most species are
less than ½ in (1·2 cm) long and are pale
brown. Only the males have two pairs of
membranous wings and occasionally they fly
to lights at night. The most characteristic
feature of the Embioptera is the presence of a
very swollen section towards the tip of the
front legs, that is the first and second tarsal
segments. This swelling contains the silk
producing glands. Fine threads of silk are
emitted from many hollow bristles on the
under-surface of the segments. When tunnels
are being constructed the front legs rapidly
cross and recross one another as the silk is
produced.

Eggs are laid in groups along the course of
the silken tunnels and the females show
similar parental care to that of earwigs. The
larvae are similar to the adults, and have well
developed silk glands. They probably feed
mainly on vegetable matter. ORDER: Embioptera, CLASS: Insecta, PHYLUM: Arthropoda.
R.F.C.

EMBRYO, a term usually restricted to the
product of the development of the fertilized
ovum (zygote) during its transformation into
a new and fully formed individual. With
unicellular organisms the visible changes
entailed by this transformation are so small
that the term is usually avoided, being applied
only to developing multicellular organisms
that, in the adult condition, show a degree of
morphological differentiation. In animals
that lay eggs, and in which most of the
developmental processes occur outside the
body of the mother, all stages up to hatching
are called embryos. The young of animals in
which the egg completes its main development within the body of the mother (usually
in the oviduct) are known as embryos until
the moment of birth. When applied to human
beings, the word embryo often refers only to
the child during early development (two to
three months); the later developmental stage
is called a foetus. To a varying extent this
same usage is applied to other mammals.

Embryology also comprehends the study
of larvae and pupae, which are regarded as
specialized embryos.

The ovum of all animals contains a
quantity, great or small, of stored food,
usually yolk, and is enclosed within a
membrane which is part of the cell itself.

he early embryos in all the vertebrate classes closely resemble each other and only later do the characteristic features of each group develop. This similarity
one of the principal indications of evolution having taken place.

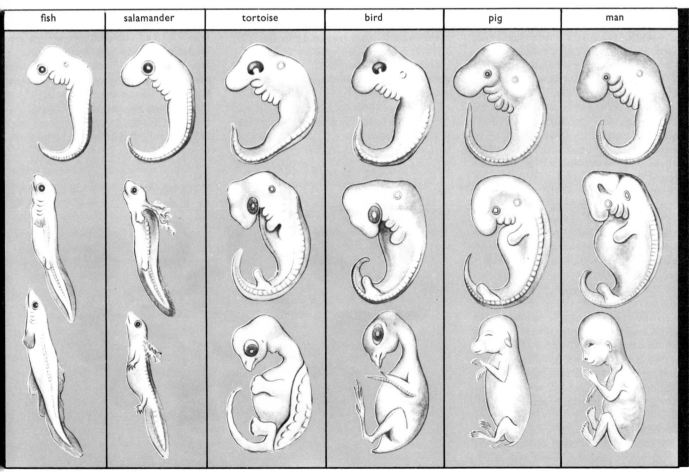

| fish | salamander | tortoise | bird | pig | man |

Additional non-cellular material is added to the outside of the ovum by the ovary. These coatings, or remains of them, persist at least for a time during development. When the egg enters the oviduct, further non-cellular material, such as a shell, is secreted around it.

Development of the embryo usually begins immediately the haploid female nucleus has fused with the haploid male nucleus. In some animals normally, and in others by experimental manipulation, an embryo will develop from an unfertilized ovum, the phenomenon being known as parthenogenesis, or 'virgin birth'.

The formation of a more or less complex multicellular organism from a single cell, the zygote, involves three general processes, growth and cell division, morphogenesis, and differentiation, but the actual manner in which the embryo develops depends very much on the type of egg and on the kind of animal to be produced. Growth of an embryo is the outcome of the utilization of stored food, to form additional living substance, the absorption of water and then the division of the enlarged cell. Early morphogenesis in chordate animals is a result of the migration of cells within the embryo, and all morphogenetic change is related to the rate of division of groups of cells of the embryo.

Differentiation is the outcome of chemical and structural alterations in groups of cells. The manner in which cells differentiate is controlled by genes, many of which operate only for a short period during development. The diversity of zygotes is enormous. Yolk may be entirely absent, as in most mammals, or where it is present the proportion of yolk to cytoplasm may vary enormously. In reptiles and birds, cytoplasm constitutes a minute part of the zygote and is separate from the yolky material. The amount of stored food greatly influences the subsequent development of the zygote. Eggs with little yolk are produced in great numbers and fertilization is external and is very much a matter of chance. The more yolk stored in the egg the more voluminous the protective envelopes secreted by the oviduct (e.g. egg white and shell in birds) and the more effective the devices to ensure fertilization (culminating in the fertilization of large yolked ova within the oviduct by copulation).

Within the cytoplasm of zygotes there is always some localization of specialized parts, but cell differentiation may be very delayed so that each of the cells after several divisions may be capable, in suitable conditions, of forming a new embryo. In many invertebrates, cell-differentiation occurs early and, at the two-cell stage, the right and left halves of the future embryo may be already unalterably laid down.

Zygotes with little, or relatively little, stored food must obviously divide (and the embryo grow, acquire shape and differ-

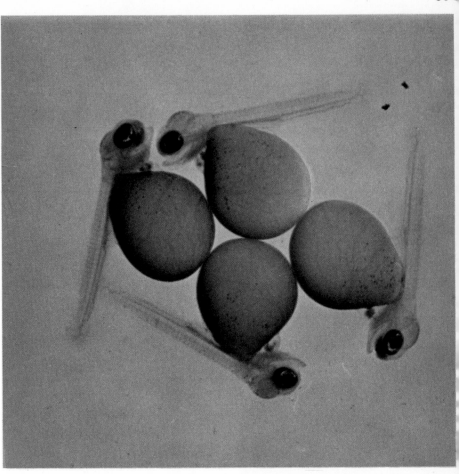

Fish embryos removed from the egg-membrane just prior to hatching, to show the large yoke-sac.

entiate) rapidly once development starts. This usually results in the formation of a larva, a developmental stage that differs radically in structure from the adult but which is able to obtain its own food.

Larvae are common among invertebrates (e.g. the caterpillar) and also Amphibia (the tadpole). A larva may acquire the adult form by further growth and gradual changes in the body (as with tadpoles) or may undergo a prolonged growth phase culminating in a non-motile pupa inside which radical change and differentiation produce the adult body. Instances are known of larvae (e.g. the axolotl) that, because of a metabolic deficiency, are unable to develop into a normal adult but nevertheless form functional sexual organs.

Embryos of *Rivulus milesi*, a freshwater fish of tropical America, seen through their egg-membranes.

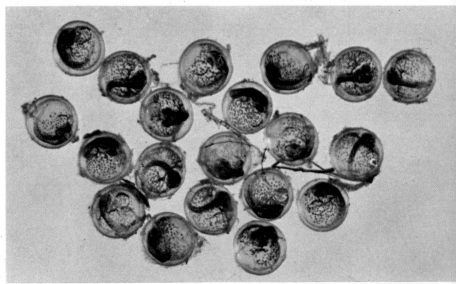

The embryos of some types of animal form special membranes as an adjunct to the embryo proper. These are discarded when the embryo hatches or is born. Such embryonic membranes do not contribute to the body of the future adult but they assist the embryo to develop. In reptiles and birds the embryonic membranes may be regarded as special structures associated with the vast amount of stored food in the egg and with the non-aquatic habitat. Such eggs contain enough food to last the developing individual during the long period of transition from the single cell to the large complicated, fully developed body. There may be so much food that it becomes contained in a yolk-sac hanging like a bag from the alimentary canal until the embryo has developed sufficiently to draw it inside.

The special membranes help in the utilization of the food and the acquisition of oxygen. They also enable the embryo proper to meet

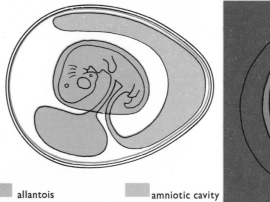
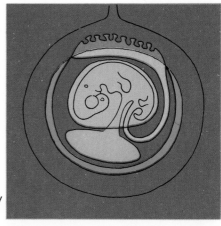

allantois

amniotic cavity

chorionic membrane

yolk-sac

The cleidoic egg (left) with the embryo surrounded by its membranes and connected to a yolk-sac. The mammalian embryo (right) is enclosed in similar membranes within the mother's uterus, attached to it by a placenta.

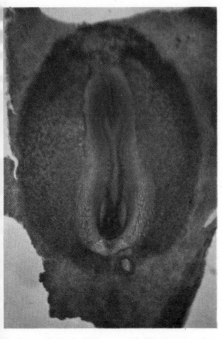

Embryo of chick 18 hours old. The head end is pointed towards the bottom of the picture. The 'tail' at the other end is the primitive streak.

the requirements of excretion and help to protect the delicate developing organism from mechanical shock, sharp temperature changes and other dangers. The outermost of these membranes is the chorion which completely encloses the embryonic system, just inside the egg-shell in reptiles and birds and inside the uterus in mammals. The embryo itself is enclosed in a fluid-containing cavity, the amniotic cavity, bordered by the amnion (which sometimes surrounds the head of the newborn infant, when it is called a caul). The allantois is an outgrowth from the urinary bladder which in placental mammals carries embryonic blood vessels to the undersurface of the chorion (in mammals called the

trophoblast), where it forms the placenta. This, made up of interlocking folds and processes, derived from the allantois and chorion, and from the uterine wall, is the organ of physiological interchange of substances between embryo and mother. It is connected with the embryo by the umbilical cord. The blood of the offspring circulates through the placenta in close proximity to that of the mother, from which it takes up food and oxygen as well as passing waste matter into the maternal blood, to be passed to the exterior through the mother's body. After birth, the placenta is shed.

As all cells need an aquatic environment, this has to be ensured for the developing embryo of terrestrial animals, at least until the relatively watertight skin has been formed. The watery environment is provided first by the various layers of secreted substance (such as the white of a hen's egg) which surround the developing zygote. Usually the whole is enclosed in a shell which reduces the loss of water. Both mechanical and chemical protection from biological attack is also afforded by these secreted substances. The development

of the amnion and chorion allows the embryo, already in a watery medium, to be contained in a special aquatic environment, the amniotic fluid, which is secreted by the living cells of the developing zygote.

In mammals, particularly human beings, the embryonic membranes are called foetal membranes. In a number of mammals the method of development and the form of the membranes are clearly similar to those of reptiles. In others, especially human beings, modified time sequences and suppression of some reptilian features make this less obvious.   A.F.

EMBRYOLOGY, the study of the structure and development of embryos. The actual process of development is usually divided into the following phases: (1) fertilization; (2) cleavage, a period of active cell division leading to the formation of a hollow ball of cells, known as the blastula; (3) gastrulation, a process of folding and intucking of the blastula resulting in a two or three layered structure, the gastrula; (4) organogeny, the formation of the organs and organ systems.

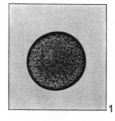
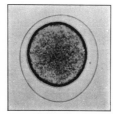
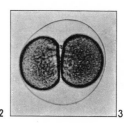
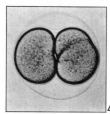

Development of *Echinus esculentus* (1) unfertilized egg, (2) fertilized egg, (3) two-cells, (4) dividing into four, (5) four cells, (6) eight cells, (7) blastula ready to hatch, (8) gastrula.

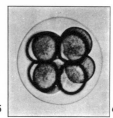
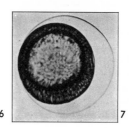
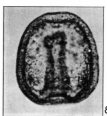

Emu, Australian running bird, flightless and with wings so small they are hidden among the feathers.

EMU *Dromaius novae-hollandiae,* the largest bird inhabiting the Australian continent, it is flightless and its tiny wings are only $\frac{1}{10}$ of the length of the bird's body. Nowadays only one species exists but at the time of the first European settlement three other island species occurred along the southern coast of Australia: the Kangaroo Island emu, the King Island emu and the Tasmanian emu. The scientific names of these three island species are much in dispute because the few existing specimens are so poorly labelled that it is difficult to sort out which specimen was collected on which island. All three species were exterminated soon after permanent settlements were established and all three were smaller than the mainland species. The King Island emu was even smaller than the Tasmanian emu, and a mere dwarf beside the mainland species. Emus are closely related to cassowaries *Casuarius,* but the relationship of both groups to other *ratite birds is tenuous and disputed.

Emus are brown although when the feathers are new after the moult they may appear nearly black, fading to pale brown with age. The bases of the feathers are white. Each feather has two indentical shafts, with the barbs so widely spaced that they do not interlock to form the firm vane as do the feathers of most birds. Rather they form a loose, hair-like body covering. The feathers growing out from the back near the base of the spine differ from those covering the rest of the bird in having longer barbs and being set very far apart indeed, looking even looser than the body feathers and giving the appearance of a mop-like 'tail'. The skin on the neck and head is often free of feathers and has a more or less bluish tinge. The intensity of this colour varies according, apparently, to the season of the year and also in response to moment to moment changes in its sur-

roundings and the behaviour of other nearby birds. The sexes are similar in plumage except in the period prior to egg laying, when the female's head and neck are densely covered with black feathers, whereas the male's head and neck are largely bare. In addition the dense white feather bases of the male's lower neck feathers are conspicuous at this time, giving his neck a striking, pale appearance, particularly from the front. Adult females weigh about 90 lb (41 kg) and males 80 lb (36 kg). The female of a pair is usually larger than the male, in other dimensions as well as body weight, although it appears that differences in rearing conditions can result in well fed males being larger than poorly fed females. The legs are unfeathered and so long that a running bird can make a stride of 9 ft (2·7 m) with ease. Emus have three toes, compared with the two of the ostrich *Struthio,* and the underside of each toe is flattened with a broad pad. The bill is broad and soft, adapted for browsing and grazing but with muscles too weak to hold any smooth heavy object. The wings, though greatly reduced in size, appear to assist the bird in cooling itself. In hot conditions they are held out from the side and the bare 'under arm', with its plexus of superficial blood vessels, is exposed to facilitate cooling by evaporation.

Emus occur throughout the Australian mainland, from the highest mountains to the coast. They are very sparse in the arid uninhabited interior but attain a density of about 1 per 5 sq miles (14 sq km) wherever artificial watering places have been provided by inland sheep farmers. They are even more common in the forested coastal regions, but absent wherever clearing is extensive, particularly in those areas where wheat and other arable crops are grown.

The birds usually breed in the winter months, May–August, throughout their range, but occasional out-of-season nests are found, particularly after rain in the interior. Most breeding units are of a single pair, but very rarely some circumstantial evidence has been found of two hens laying in the same nest, but this is not common. The nest is a low platform of twigs or leaves, generally placed so that the sitting bird has a clear outlook, often downhill. The early eggs of the clutch are covered and left, and the male does not begin sitting until between five and nine eggs have been laid. The interval between the laying of successive eggs probably varies with seasonal conditions, being longer in poor seasons; under good but not excellent conditions it is four days. Under such conditions a hen will lay from 9–12 eggs, each weighing 1–1½ lb (0·5–0·7 kg), but in very good seasons the clutch may exceed 20, and in poor seasons be as low as four or five. It is likely that young birds lay smaller clutches than older birds under the same

seasonal conditions. Once the female has laid the clutch the male carries out the whole incubation process. Incubation takes about eight weeks from the time he begins to sit and during this time he hardly eats and does not drink. Indeed he seldom leaves the nest rising daily only to turn the eggs. The incubation temperature of 91°F (33°C) is low compared with that of most birds.

The tiny chicks leave the nest after two or three days and may often be seen leading their father rather than being led by him. They feed extensively on green vegetation and insects during their first weeks and grow rapidly. At first their plumage is cream with brown longitudinal stripes, and dark dots on the head, but as they grow the stripes become less conspicuous and the chicks gradually acquire a dappled appearance, differing from their parents in the dense black feathering of the head. They are capable of breeding at 22 months old, but in the arid inland of Australia often accompany their parent for 18 months, and probably do not breed until at least their third year.

Adult emus feed mainly on fruits, flowers, insects, seeds and green vegetation. Caterpillars are favoured whenever they are available and beetles and grasshoppers are taken in large quantities when they are abundant. The seeds and pods of many pea-like shrubs and trees are a staple food source in summer. The large fruits of a wide variety of shrubs and trees of other species, differing from locality to locality, are commonly eaten in the spring. Grass and herbage form the bulk of the autumn and winter food and emus will sometimes graze clover leys at this season. They do not, except under conditions of extreme drought, browse shrub leaves or eat dried vegetation. Quite large stones are ingested into the gizzard to aid the grinding process and single pebbles of 1 in (2·5 cm) in diameter are not unusual. Some of these stones are probably carried inside the bird for long periods and marbles, fed to zoo birds, have been retained for three months before excretion.

The birds have two main calls, a guttural grunt and a throbbing drum. Despite many statements to the contrary, both sexes are capable of giving both types of call. However, the grunts are most commonly given by the male during the two or three months prior to egg laying, over the period during which copulation can be observed. The drumming call is frequently given during the same period, and again by the hen towards the end of incubation. Both sexes drum when mildly alarming stimuli are present, for example when approaching an artificial waterpoint or when investigating a strange object.

The emu does not appear to be an endangered species while such large areas of its forest, savannah and heathland habitat are

retained in their present, near-virgin state. On the other hand it is sometimes responsible for damage to wheat fields at harvest time, particularly in Western Australia. If the population of the arid inland is large and the inland experiences a dry winter, large numbers of emus move southwest, invading the wheat farms and trampling the crops. The Western Australian Government has erected long fences to deflect the migrating birds. The emus travel hundreds of miles on these southwesterly migrations and the survivors appear to make a return migration northeast during the summer, particularly if a cyclone brings summer rain to the arid inland. In eastern Australia similar movements probably occur, but on a much smaller scale for the arid inland is there dissected by large rivers and watercourses. Even though these rivers may not flow throughout the summer, their banks and flood plains remain relatively damp and apparently support sufficient vegetation to prevent the emus moving into the wheat farms to the southeast. No migrations have been reported from eastern Australia on the scale of those witnessed in Western Australia.

Emu carcasses dress to about 30 lb (13·5 kg) of lean meat and the large numbers, tens of thousands, that are involved in some of the migrations in Western Australia are a protein source that has yet to be exploited. When the timing and extent of these movements can be predicted accurately, it should be relatively easy to harvest and process tons of meat. At present the carcasses are left to rot in the sun after the migrating birds have been shot to protect the wheat farms. FAMILY: Dromaiidae, ORDER: Casuariiformes, CLASS: Aves.   S.J.J.F.D.

ENDOCRINE GLANDS, or ductless glands, structures which secrete chemical messengers or hormones directly into the blood stream. Such glands occur not only in mammals and other vertebrate animals, but also throughout the animal kingdom, notably in insects, Crustacea, annelid worms and molluscs.

There are two main kinds of endocrine glands—those arising from epithelial tissue and those derived from transformed nerve cells. In addition to compact endocrine organs, there are also secretory cells actually within the nervous system. These so-called neurosecretory cells have all the appearance of nerve cells, but they differ from them in that their axons neither make connexions with other nerve cells nor innervate effector organs. Instead they end in swollen bulbs which are usually in close contact with the blood system. Unlike ordinary nerve cells which secrete acetyl choline or adrenalin,

Emus drinking. Dry seasons cause the emus to migrate, unless there are watercourses available.

neurosecretory cells produce hormones which are usually small peptides. Neurosecretory cells have been found in every group of animals from coelenterates to man, and constitute the most primitive system, in the evolutionary sense, enabling the animal to react to changes in its environment as perceived by its sense organs.

As epithelial endocrine glands are evolved, they remain controlled by neurosecretory cells. The vertebrate hypothalamo-hypophysial system provides the major example of such a system. The hypophysis or *pituitary is divided into two main regions, the epithelial adenohypophysis (which includes the so-named anterior and intermediate lobes) and neurohypophysis or posterior pituitary. The neurohypophysis is derived from and is continuous with the part of the underside of the brain known as the hypothalamus. The posterior pituitary hormones are, indeed, probably formed with little change from substances which pass down the axons of the hypothalamic neurosecretory cells into the posterior pituitary. The anterior pituitary, on the other hand, receives no nerves from the hypothalamus, it is connected with it solely by blood vessels known as the hypophysial portal system. The secretion by the anterior pituitary is entirely controlled by a series of releasing—or sometimes inhibiting—factors, which pass through this system from the hypothalamus.

The anterior pituitary, in turn, produces a series of so-called trophic hormones which control most, though not all, of the remaining endocrine glands. Thus the anterior pitu-

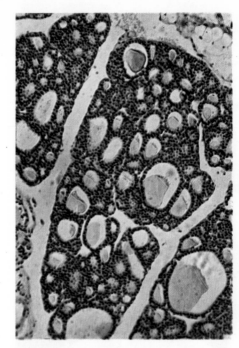

Section through a thyroid gland, one of the endocrine or ductless glands.

itary produces adrenocorticotrophic hormone (ACTH) which acts on the adrenal cortex, and thyrotrophic hormone (TSH), which causes enlargement of the thyroid and the release of thyroid hormone. It also secretes three gonadotrophic hormones. The first, follicle stimulating hormone (FSH) stimulates development of the ovarian follicles in the female and maturation of spermatozoa in the male. The second, luteinizing hormone (LH) induces the formation from

developed ovarian follicles of a transitory endocrine organ known as the corpus luteum, which is concerned through its secretions with the maintenance of pregnancy. The third, prolactin or lactogenic hormone (LH) is necessary—with other hormones— to bring the mammary glands into secretion and may also be essential for maintaining the corpus luteum in a secretory state. The remaining anterior pituitary secretion is growth hormone or somatotrophin (STH) which causes growth of the skeleton and muscles. It is sometimes also called diabetogenic hormone because it acts on the pancreas to cause a rise in blood sugar. The intermediate lobe of the pituitary produces factors—melanocyte stimulating hormone (MSH)—which affect skin colour.

The hypothalamo-hypophysial system provides a two-tiered mechanism by which the various endocrine glands of the body are controlled and influenced by the environment. Thus, in mammals and birds both the reproductive season and moulting are controlled by factors such as seasonal changes in the duration of daylight. The pineal gland, on the upper side of the brain, is also concerned in these interactions. Within the body the whole system is self-regulatory, in the sense that increased secretion of hormones by endocrine glands acts on the hypothalamo-hypophysial system to reduce the output of trophic hormones—a so-called negative *feedback system.

The main endocrine glands, which are subsidiary to the hypothalamo-hypophysial system, are the thyroid, situated in the neck, the adrenal bodies, lying near the kidneys

The hormone-producing glands in the human body. 1. The thyroid, 2. reproductive glands (ovary and testis), 3. the adrenals, 4. islets of Langerhans, oval or spherical bodies scattered throughout the pancreas, concerned with the metabolism of sugar, 5. the hypophysis or pituitary which occupies a central place in the control of all the endocrine glands.

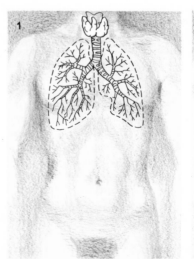

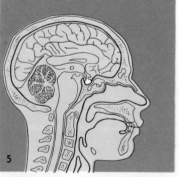
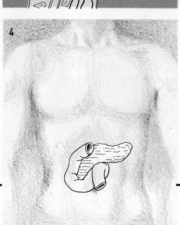
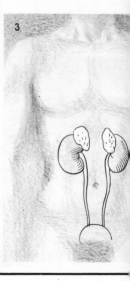

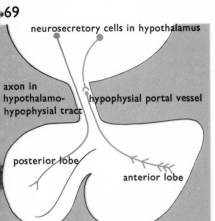

The endocrine system in mammals provides a two-tiered mechanism for control by the environment.

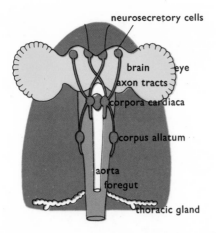

Insects have a series of endocrine glands (red) analogous to though simpler than that of vertebrates.

the male testes and the female ovaries. Other endocrine glands are the pancreas, concerned in the control of the level of blood sugar and in its utilization, and the parathyroid, situated in or near the thyroids and controlling the distribution of calcium between the bones, blood and other tissues. Parts of the gut also secrete hormones; secretin which induces pancreatic secretion and is itself produced by the jujeunum, was the first hormone to be clearly defined.

Insects have a series of endocrine glands analogous to, though simpler than, the system in vertebrates. The brain of insects contains groups of neurosecretory cells, and nerve axons run ventrally from them into a pair of glands known as the corpora cardiaca, or into a further pair known as the corpora allata. It seems likely that neurosecretory material synthesized in the brain cells actually passes into the corpora cardiaca. Insects have a third pair of endocrine organs known as thoracic glands which have no direct connexion with the remaining endocrine system, but work closely with it. The corpora cardiaca produce hormones which affect heart beat, carbohydrate utilization and protein synthesis, while the corpora allata produce juvenile hormone (neotenin) which affects the course of larval development, and the thoracic glands produce ecdysone or moulting hormone.

A range of endocrine glands occurs in other animal groups. Crustacea have groups of neurosecretory cells in the brain which send their axons to sinus glands in the eyestalks, and to post-commissural organs behind the brain, which are thus analagous to the insect corpora cardiaca or the vertebrate posterior pituitary. Worms also have neurosecretory cells in the brain and nervous system; their secretions control growth, regeneration and reproduction. Thus the tail of a headless ragworm will not regenerate in the normal fashion; the brain is necessary. Molluscs similarly have neurosecretory cells, but neither worms nor molluscs—with the ex-

ception of cephalopods—appear to have any epithelial endocrine glands. In squids and octopods, however, optic glands lying between the eyes have been shown to control the onset of sexual maturity.   F.J.E.

ENDODERM, the innermost germ layer of an embryo. In coelenterates it forms the inner cell-layer of the adult, in which it is still usually referred to as the endoderm although the term endodermis is sometimes used. In animals above the coelenterate level of organization, the endoderm gives rise to the thin lining layer of the gut, except for a short stretch at each end, and contributes to certain glands, such as the liver, which arise as outgrowths of the gut. In vertebrates the lining of the lungs is also of endodermal origin.

ENDOPARASITES, parasites which live in the body of the host. They usually occupy the gut, body cavity and blood system but some live in the muscles or nervous systems. The anatomy of endoparasites is often much modified with reduction or loss of sense organs, limbs and gut. Food is often absorbed straight from the host's tissues and the parasite may be little more than a bag of reproductive organs. The life-cycle is often very complicated with the production of vast numbers of eggs and larval stages. See parasites.

ENERGY, an abstract concept describing the capacity of any system to do work, that is—in the simplest mechanical terms—to change the velocity of a moving body. It was Sir Isaac Newton who first formulated the idea that moving bodies remain in motion unless an outside force acts on them and in doing so he put forward the idea of momentum, namely mass × velocity, to describe this property. If a moving body collides with a stationary one and sets it in motion,

as when one billiard ball strikes another, momentum is transferred, but the total momentum remains the same. If, however, the body is brought to rest by frictional forces its momentum (mv) or 'kinetic energy' ($\frac{1}{2}$ mv^2) becomes converted into heat. Other forms of energy are light and electrical current and all forms of energy are capable of interconversion.

Living matter makes use of the energy in the chemical bonds which hold the atoms together in a molecule. When a chemical reaction takes place at a constant temperature and pressure, any heat produced will be conducted away, and any gas involved will simply do work against the atmosphere. Only the remaining so-called 'free-energy' will be available within the system for other purposes. Most, although not all, of the energy-yielding reactions of living organisms are oxidations of carbohydrates—substances like starch and sugars. Such energy is carried between the sites of intracellular processes by special molecules, of which adenosine triphosphate or ATP is the most important.

ATP is unstable, and its molecule can readily be hydrolyzed by a molecule of water to form adenosine diphosphate (ADP) plus a molecule of phosphoric acid:

$$ATP + H_2O = ADP + H_2PO_3$$

This change of state makes available 8,900 calories of free-energy per molecular weight in grams of ATP; i.e. the free-energy or ΔF is said to be $-8,900$ cal/mole.

Adenosine diphosphate is reconverted to adenosine triphosphate by the oxidation of carbohydrates. For example, the total conversion of glucose to carbon dioxide and water:

$$C6H_{12}O_6 + 6O_2 \longrightarrow 6CO_2 + 6H_2O$$

yields 685,600 cal/mole of free-energy. ($\Delta F_1 = -685,600$ cal/mole). In fact, the process generates 38 energy-rich bonds of ATP. Since each is worth 8,900 calories it is easy to calculate that the total is 338,200 cal/mole and represents an efficiency of about 50%. The stages by which carbohydrates, and other compounds, yield this energy are summarized elsewhere (see Kreb's cycle).

All life depends ultimately on energy from the sun. The sources of free-energy are constantly replaced by the process of photosynthesis which takes place in green plants. In essence, the energy becomes stored in the chemical bonds of carbohydrates, which are built up in plants from carbon dioxide and water. The energy of sunlight is captured by the aid of a substance known as chlorophyll, which must thus be considered one of the key substances to life.   F.J.G.E.

ENGRAVER BEETLES, or Bark beetles are closely related to both the weevils and the Ambrosia beetles. The females burrow through the bark of trees, such as pine or elm, and then they excavate a large chamber or egg gallery. Along the edge of this chamber eggs are deposited each of which hatches into a wood eating larva. These larvae tunnel into the wood to produce a burrow of increasing diameter, as one might expect as the larvae are growing in size. When fully grown the larvae pupate and hatch into adult beetles which then have to burrow their way out of the timber. The adults then mate and infest a new tree.

Many of these beetles cause serious damage to timber and one species transmits the fungus disease Dutch elm disease which is fatal to those trees it infects. FAMILY: Scolytidae, ORDER: Coleoptera, CLASS: Insecta, PHYLUM: Arthropoda.

ENSIGN WASPS, a small family of some 200 species. Their common name reflects their rather bizarre appearance, for the abdomen, laterally compressed and disc-shaped, attached to the thorax by a long stalk-like 'waist', is reminiscent of a flag being held aloft. The larvae of these wasps are parasitic in the eggs of various insects, especially cockroaches. FAMILY: Evaniidae, ORDER: Hymenoptera, CLASS: Insecta, PHYLUM: Arthropoda.

ENTAMOEBA, a parasitic amoeba found in many animals including man and sometimes causing disease. Several species of *Entamoeba* have been recorded and the best known are *E. invadens* from snakes, *E. ranarum* from frogs, especially the tadpoles, and *E. histolytica* from man. All these amoebae are fairly small and inhabit the intestines of their hosts where they move over the surface of the epithelium feeding on bacteria and detritus and forming cysts which pass to the outside to infect new hosts. *E. histolytica* has a world-wide distribution in man in whom it is usually quite harmless. Under certain conditions which have not yet been defined the amoebae invade the epithelial cells of the intestine and form ulcers. The effect of this invasion is a condition known as amoebic dysentery, which becomes complicated as the ulcers involve blood vessels. Amoebae may enter the damaged blood vessels and get carried to other parts of the body where they set up what is known as metastatic infections. These occur chiefly in the liver, causing hepatic amoebiasis, but also elsewhere. Both the intestinal and the metastatic forms may be fatal.

Although *E. histolytica* is found throughout the world it seems to be pathogenic only in the tropics. The reason for this is not known for certain, but it may be due to differences in diet. The study of the pathogenicity of *E. histolytica* is complicated by the fact that there also exists in man another species, *E. hartmanni,* which is morphologically similar, but is smaller and never causes

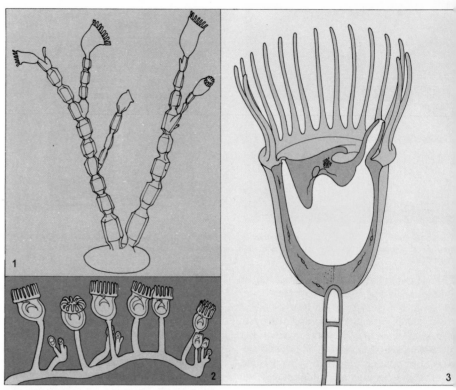

1. *Urnatella,* the only freshwater entoproct. 2. Colony of the marine entoproct *Pedicellina cernus* The extremities of the branching stolon produce buds which develop into stalked zooids, each bearing up to 24 tentacles. 3. Typical entoproct calyx showing internal structures.

any disease. ORDER: Amoebida, CLASS: Sarcodina, PHYLUM: Protozoa.   F.E.G.C.

ENTOMOLOGY, the name given to that branch of biology dealing with the study of insects. In a broader sense the term is sometimes erroneously used to cover studies on groups of arthropods other than insects, for example, myriapods (millipedes and centipedes) and arachnids.

ENTOPROCTA, phylum of tiny colonial animals comprising a handful of marine genera, notably *Pedicellina* and *Loxosomella* and the freshwater genus *Urnatella*. The marine Entoprocta, though diminutive and rarely exceeding $\frac{1}{16}$ in (2 mm) in length, are not at all rare on the shore and in shallow water. *Pedicellina* is the most familiar genus and was the first to be discovered. Being a colonial organism made up of tentaculated zooids, each one containing a deeply looped gut with separate mouth and anus, *Pedicellina* was placed initially in the phylum Bryozoa. When its anatomy had been better studied, the separate phylum Entoprocta (later unnecessarily renamed Kamptozoa) was created for *Pedicellina*.

Pedicellina has a world-wide distribution and occurs in little clumps on sea-weeds at low tidemark, and on pier piles and similar structures. The zooids are usually of one sex only. Gonads are paired, lying one on each side of the nerve ganglion. In the female a hollow region occupying the loop of the gut

acts as a brood chamber in which the embryos develop. They are later liberated a trochophore larvae which can metamorphose and found a new colony. In many entoproct the larva already displays the organization o an adult.   J.S.R.

ENVIRONMENT, the surroundings of an organism, the place in which it lives. The study of the relationship between organism and their environments is called ecology. In a sense the environment of every organism is the whole world, since all organisms everywhere are involved in the great globa processes of the cycling of chemicals and the flow of energy. But during evolution each species of animal or plant has become specialized or adapted in such a way that it can carry out its processes of life efficiently only in certain parts of the world where particular climatic factors and food resources occur. Ecologists call these places the 'habitat' of a species and its habitat affects an organism much more than the rest of the greater global environment. Generally a habitat contains many species of organisms all of which are adapted to live in the environment and these are termed the biotic community of the habitat. Each species of the community is part of the environment of all the others and affects all of them in some way. Different terrestrial habitats are usually easily recognizable and are often defined by the most prominent plants living in them, e.g. woodland or forest, grassland, but in the sea habitats are very much harder to distinguish.

Some species can be found in several different habitats and are members of the biotic community of each. Species like these must be able to live in the climatic conditions and with the food resources of all of these habitats and are said to be 'ecologically-tolerant' or 'eurytopic' species. But most species can live only in the conditions provided by one or two habitats and are said to be 'stenotopic'. Very often a species cannot live in the conditions provided by its habitat as a whole but only in a small part of it – this is called the 'microhabitat' of a species. Woodland, for instance, contains many hundreds of such microhabitats, such as the soil, the leaf litter layer above it, short vegetation, shrubs, the leaf canopy of the trees, tree trunks, underneath bark, in the axils of branches and many more, and each of these contains a number of species which are specially adapted to live in them. A biotic community of a habitat and its environment form a very intimate association and chemical substances and energy are constantly passing between them. This is termed an ecosystem.

Organisms are affected by many different factors in their environment, and the ones that limit a species to a particular part of the environment are called its 'limiting factors'. During its evolution each species has become adapted to function within a particular combination of limiting factors and so, strictly, it is limited not by the factors themselves but by its own physiology. Nevertheless, it is very convenient to analyze a species' relations with its environment in terms of such factors.

What are these limiting factors? First, there are physical or abiotic factors which consist primarily of the climate of the habitat and the structural material from which it is made – mineral materials, especially rocks, water and atmospheric gases. Second, there are biotic factors, consisting of interactions between the species in the community and their food resources.

Physical factors of the environment. One of the most important of these for organisms is temperature. This is because all chemical reactions are influenced by temperature, being stimulated or quickened by high temperatures and slowed by low ones. The particular combination of chemicals which we call life can remain combined over only a limited range of temperatures and breaks down at extremes. Although certain bacteria can tolerate temperatures up to 185°F (85°C) and some insects can remain active at temperatures as low as 14°F (−10°C), the great majority of organisms live within a temperature range from about 32–104°F (0°C to 40°C). Any particular species can rarely tolerate a temperature range greater than about 87°F (30°C), in most cases much

less. Most animals and all plants are 'cold-blooded' or poikilothermic. That is, the temperature of their bodies is the same or nearly the same as that of their environments. But the mammals and birds are 'warm-blooded' or homoiothermic and have developed mechanisms for keeping their bodies at a fairly high, constant temperature, generally between 87–104°F (30–40°C). They do this by covering themselves with insulating materials, hair or feathers and by methods for producing heat internally in cold environments or for cooling themselves in hot ones. Warm-bloodedness gives the advantages of keeping all the processes of life working at a high rate all the time and has undoubtedly been largely responsible for the great importance of birds and mammals, including our own species, in the world today.

Water is important to organisms because it is the universal solute in which all their chemical processes such as digestion and respiration occur. Nearly all organisms have over half of their matter made up of water and some, especially aquatic ones, have much more; it is one of the few substances that can pass directly through the membranes which surround cells. Plants take in their mineral nutrients from the soil dissolved in water and many animals, too, require their food to be dissolved or suspended in water, or at least moistened. It is probable that the first forms of life evolved in watery environments and that is where we find the simplest forms of life today. These simple organisms have little ability to control the amount of water in their bodies and its movement into and out of their cells. More advanced forms of life have evolved much greater control over these problems of water balance. The physical process of osmosis by which water will move through membranes like those surrounding the cells of animals and plants from a weak solution of salts to a strong one exerts a great influence on organisms. Many animals that live in the salty environment of the sea have body fluids which are much the same in salt concentration as the sea. But most fish, for instance, have body fluids that are more dilute than sea water and so are likely to be dehydrated by the passage of water from their tissues to the sea. To counteract this they have skins which are rather impermeable to water and are also covered in scales and a slimy substance called mucus; they are also able to 'drink' sea water. All animals living in fresh water, on the other hand, have body fluids which have a much higher concentration of salts than their surroundings and are therefore liable to be 'flooded' by water coming into their tissues. They cope with this problem by having impermeable skins and by evolving pumping mechanisms to remove excess water from their bodies. Animals living in such places as estuaries may have to survive in environments which are alternately

salty or fresh and are exposed to the risks of both dehydration and flooding.

Organisms living on dry land, terrestrial organisms, are not faced with the problems of osmotic processes, but with the hazards of dehydration because of the drying powers of the air. Very few groups of animals have been able to solve this problem. Only the insects and arachnids (spiders and scorpions), which have evolved a waxy, waterproof covering, the cuticle, and the reptiles, mammals and birds, with a waterproof skin and a covering of scales, hair or feathers, have been able to live successfully in the terrestrial environment. Most other animals found on land, e.g. some Crustacea (woodlice) and earthworms, can do so only by remaining in places such as the soil where they will not become desiccated. Most terrestrial animals can also take up water from their environments by drinking to make up for that lost by evaporation from these surfaces or in the excretion of waste products. The amount of water actually present in terrestrial environments varies greatly and animals and plants need special adaptations to live in both very wet environments such as marshlands and in dry ones like deserts. The main factor causing this variation is rainfall or precipitation and this varies from an inch or so (a few cm) per year or less in deserts to over 80 in (200 cm) in some equatorial countries. Consequently, organisms adapted to different amounts of water in their environments, like those adapted to different ranges of temperature, are unevenly distributed in the environment.

Atmospheric gases. Most organisms are affected by the concentration of atmospheric gases in their environment. The most important of these is oxygen, since nearly all organisms use it in the chemical processes involved in the release of energy from their food. Oxygen makes up 21 per cent of atmospheric air and in most terrestrial habitats does not become depleted because plants produce it as a by-product of their processes of 'fixing' energy from sunlight (photosynthesis). Most terrestrial animals therefore have an adequate supply of oxygen which they can take into solution in their body fluids in the process of respiration for which most have special structural modifications. In a few places where plants are absent, such as caves and deep in the soil (and also at high altitudes), oxygen may fall to only five or six per cent of the atmosphere; organisms living here have special adaptations to survive the conditions and some, called anaerobes, can obtain energy from their food without oxygen. Aquatic organisms draw on oxygen dissolved in the water, but there is much less oxygen available here because for chemical reasons a given volume of water can never contain more than $\frac{1}{25}$ of the oxygen of the same volume of air. This means that aquatic organisms are much more frequently exposed to conditions where the concentration of oxygen is too low for their activities than are terrestrial organisms, A further problem is that warm water contains much less oxygen than cold water; water at 87°F (30°C) contains only half the oxygen of water at 32°F (0°C). This is why animals in small freshwater ponds often die in hot weather – literally, they suffocate from lack of oxygen – and why tropical aquaria must be supplied continuously with oxygen. (This is a good illustration of the way in which environmental factors, in this case temperature and oxygen concentration, interact in their influence on organisms). Carbon dioxide is a vital environmental factor because it is a raw material in the nutrition of all green plants upon which all organisms ultimately depend for their food (see food chains). It is also given off by all organisms in their respiration. Normally it comprises only about 0·03 per cent of the atmosphere and in terrestrial situations is rarely either too high or too low for animals. It may often be important in aquatic situations since carbon dioxide combines chemically with water to form carbonic acid. This increases the acidity of the water, and since most organisms are adapted to a particular level of acidity, may often affect organisms adversely. (Acidity of the soil, which is also often influenced by the solution of carbon dioxide in the water it contains, is a very important environmental factor for most plants, and also for a few animals, especially earthworms). The concentration of carbon dioxide in water also often exerts an effect on the functioning of some marine animals, some processes being stimulated by high concentrations and others depressed. The other gases of the atmosphere are rarely important environmental factors for animals or plants, although concentrations of naturally-produced poisonous gases like methane and hydrogen sulphide are toxic to most animals, but do not occur frequently.

Light is one of the major environmental factors influencing organisms and the only important source of light in natural situations is the sun. Nearly all the energy used by the organisms of the world, including man, derives from sunlight, from which it is absorbed by green plants in photosynthesis (see food chains and webs), and this is its greatest significance as an ecological factor. But it is also the main source of heat in the world and the uneven distribution of sunlight, due to the angle of orientation of the earth to the sun, is the biggest single factor affecting climate. Light differs from most other environmental factors in being strongly directional, that is, it tends to strike organisms from only one angle, that facing the sun; this is why land plants grow upwards and most aquatic plants live close to the water surface. It is also extremely variable, both from place to place (because of geographical position

and shading by plants and topographic features such as hills) and from time to time, through the day or seasonally. The most obvious importance of light to animals is that it enables them to see each other and has therefore permitted the evolution of many kinds of complex behaviour, including all behaviour concerned in any way with vision or light sensitivity. Some organisms also use light as a signal for the initiation of various sorts of behaviour. For example, animals which do most of their feeding at twilight become active when light intensity falls below a certain level at sunset, and birds probably start their migrations when the length of daylight reaches a certain minimum level. Most green plants, and also a few animals, are influenced not only by the intensity of sunlight but also by its wavelength or spectral composition; a few are also affected by non-visible radiations from the sun, such as ultraviolet and infrared. Ultraviolet kills bacteria and is harmful to animals with little pigment like man, in which it produces sunburn. The concentration of light falls off rapidly away from the surface in water and in soil and animals living in deep oceans and in the soil are adapted to habitats with little or no light; they are frequently damaged by exposure to light but how this damage is caused is not really known.

Pressure increases rapidly with depth in water because of its high density; in the deepest oceans pressure is over 1,000 times that at the surface, and is about one ton per sq cm. Animals can survive at these depths because they contain no atmospheric gases and the pressure in their bodies is the same as that outside, but surface animals cannot penetrate far below the surface without ill effects caused by compression of their tissues. On land atmospheric pressure decreases with increase in altitude, but since so few creatures live in these places the ecological significance of them is small.

The concentration of salts in their environment, or salinity, is a very important factor for aquatic organisms but this mostly affects them through the process of osmosis which was dealt with in the discussion of water problems. Many animals are also affected by the materials of which their habitat is made, such as density of water or compaction of soil, and on a larger scale by the nature of its terrain.

Biotic factors. The biotic factors of a species' habitat are its food resources, the species that compete with it for these resources and its predators and diseases. Earlier, we compared organisms to very complex chemical compounds, but the compounds of which organisms are made are constantly undergoing chemical reactions, especially reactions which involve the expenditure of large amounts of energy. All of the processes which

living things carry out, such as growth, movement and reproduction, require supplies of potential energy. Green plants obtain their potential energy from energy contained in sunlight, but animals obtain theirs from chemical compounds in plants or other animals which they take in as food. Organisms also require compounds from which they can manufacture new tissues, and these too they obtain from their food. Although there are only a few compounds from which animals can obtain energy or building materials, these can be arranged and combined in a very large number of ways so that a large number of potential food resources (i.e. all other animals and plants) are available to a species. However, just as each species is adapted to function in only a certain range of physical factors, so each can use only a certain range of foods. Not only are most species either vegetarian or carnivorous, but most are also able to use only certain plant or animal foods. A few omnivorous species can use a wider range of foods than most others. The presence of suitable food resources is one of the most important environmental factors determining whether a species can or cannot survive in a habitat.

Although each animal species is specialized in its food requirements, there are a great many species (at least 1,300,000). Since food resources are in short supply in nearly all environments, any individual must compete for these both with other individuals of its own species and with many other species. Only those individuals and species which are able to compete successfully obtain enough resources and survive to reproduce themselves. Many species that have been unable to compete with more efficient ones have become extinct in the course of evolution. It is probable that the pressures of competition are the biggest single factor causing species to become more specialized in their requirements for habitat and food, because specialization reduces the number of competitors of a species. So if a species is to live in its habitat not only must it contain food, but also it must not contain too many competing species; this is another important limiting factor.

Nearly all animal species also provide food for other species, their predators. Parasites of all sorts, which includes disease-causing organisms such as bacteria and viruses, are also predators, but are smaller than their victims and are generally carried within their bodies. Predators and diseases are major limiting factors in the environment of nearly all species, much as diseases like yellow fever malaria or sleeping sickness have in the past limited the ability of the human species to exploit certain parts of the tropics. See food chains and webs, adaptive radiation, autecology and synecology, biogeochemical cycles, biosphere, ecosystems, ecological niche, tolerance range.   I.N.H